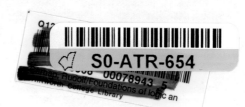

INTERNATIONAL ENCYCLOPEDIA *of* UNIFIED SCIENCE

Foundations of Logic
and
Mathematics

Rudolf Carnap

VOLUMES I AND II · FOUNDATIONS OF THE UNITY OF SCIENCE

VOLUME I · NUMBER 3

International Encyclopedia of Unified Science

Editor-in-Chief   Otto Neurath
Associate Editors   Rudolf Carnap   Charles Morris

Foundations of the Unity of Science

(Volumes I–II of the Encyclopedia)

Committee of Organization

RUDOLF CARNAP	CHARLES MORRIS
PHILIPP FRANK	OTTO NEURATH
JOERGEN JOERGENSEN	LOUIS ROUGIER

Advisory Committee

NIELS BOHR	R. VON MISES
EGON BRUNSWIK	G. MANNOURY
J. CLAY	ERNEST NAGEL
JOHN DEWEY	ARNE NESS
FEDERIGO ENRIQUES	HANS REICHENBACH
HERBERT FEIGL	ABEL REY
CLARK L. HULL	BERTRAND RUSSELL
WALDEMAR KAEMPFFERT	L. SUSAN STEBBING
VICTOR F. LENZEN	ALFRED TARSKI
JAN LUKASIEWICZ	EDWARD C. TOLMAN
WILLIAM M. MALISOFF	JOSEPH H. WOODGER

THE UNIVERSITY OF CHICAGO PRESS, CHICAGO 60637
The University of Chicago Press, Ltd., London

81   19 18 17 16

Contents:

Contents

Foundations of Logic and Mathematics

Rudolf Carnap

I. Logical Analysis of Language: Semantics and Syntax

1. Theoretical Procedures in Science

The activities of a scientist are in part practical: he arranges experiments and makes observations. Another part of his work is theoretical: he formulates the results of his observations in sentences, compares the results with those of other observers, tries to explain them by a theory, endeavors to confirm a theory proposed by himself or somebody else, makes predictions with the help of a theory, etc. In these theoretical activities, deduction plays an important part; this includes calculation, which is a special form of deduction applied to numerical expressions. Let us consider, as an example, some theoretical activities of an astronomer. He describes his observations concerning a certain planet in a report, O_1. Further, he takes into consideration a theory T concerning the movements of planets. (Strictly speaking, T would have to include, for the application to be discussed, laws of some other branches of physics, e.g., concerning the astronomical instruments used, refraction of light in the atmosphere, etc.) From O_1 and T, the astronomer deduces a prediction, P; he calculates the apparent position of the planet for the next night. At that time he will make a new observation and formulate it in a report O_2. Then he will compare the prediction P with O_2 and thereby find it either confirmed or not. If T was a new theory and the purpose of the procedure described was to test T, then the astronomer will take the confirmation of P by O_2 as a partial confirmation for T; he will apply the same procedure again and again and thereby obtain either an increasing degree of confirmation for T or else a disconfirmation. The same deduction of P from O_1 and T is made in the case where T is already scientifically acknowledged on the basis of previous evidence, and the present purpose is to obtain a prediction of what will happen tomorrow. There is a third situation in which a deduction of this kind may be made. Suppose we have made both the observations described in O_1 and in O_2; we are surprised by the results of the observation described in O_2 and therefore want an explanation for it. This explanation is given by the theory T; more precisely, by deducing P from O_1 and T and then showing that O_2 is in accordance with P ("What we have observed is exactly what we had to expect").

These simple examples show that the chief theoretical procedures in science—namely, testing a theory, giving an explanation for a known fact, and predicting an unknown fact—involve as an essential component deduction and calculation; in other words, the application of logic and mathematics. (These procedures will later be discussed more in detail, especially in §§ 15, 19, and 23.) It is one of the chief tasks of this essay to make clear the role of logic and mathematics as applied in empirical science. We shall see that they furnish instruments for deduction, that is, for the transformation of formulations of factual, contingent knowledge. However, logic and mathematics not only supply rules for transformation of factual sentences but they themselves contain sentences of a different, nonfactual kind. Therefore, we shall have to deal with the question of the nature of logical and mathematical theorems. It will become clear that they do not possess any factual content. If we call them true, then another kind of truth is meant, one not dependent upon facts. A theorem of mathematics is not tested like a theorem of physics, by deriving more and more predictions with its help and then comparing them with the results of observations. But what else is the basis of their validity? We shall try to answer these questions by examining how theorems of logic and mathematics are used in the context of empirical science.

The material on which the scientist works in his theoretical activities consists of reports of observations, scientific laws and theories, and predictions; that is, formulations in language which describe certain features of facts. Therefore, an analysis of theoretical procedures in science must concern itself with language and its applications. In the present section, in preparing for the later task, we shall outline an analysis of language and explain the chief factors involved. Three points of view will be distinguished, and accordingly three disciplines applying them, called pragmatics, semantics, and syntax. These will be illustrated by the analysis of a simple, fictitious language. In the later sections the results of these discussions will be applied in an analysis of the theoretical procedure of science, especially from the point of view of calculi, their interpretation, and their application in empirical science.

2. Analysis of Language

A language, as, e.g., English, is a system of activities or, rather, of habits, i.e., dispositions to certain activities, serving mainly for the purposes of communication and of co-ordination of activities among the members of a group. The elements of the language are signs, e.g., sounds or written marks, produced by members of the group in order to be perceived by other members and to influence their behavior. Since our final interest in this essay concerns the language of science, we shall restrict ourselves to the theoretical side of language, i.e., to the use of language for making assertions. Thus, among the different kinds of sentences, e.g., commands, questions, exclamations, declarations, etc., we shall deal with declarative sentences only. For the sake of brevity we shall call them here simply *sentences*.

This restriction to declarative sentences does not involve, in the investigation of processes accompanying the use of language, a restriction to theoretical thinking. Declarative sentences, e.g., 'This apple is sour', are connected not only with the theoretical side of behavior but also with emotional, volitional, and other factors. If we wish to investigate a language as a human activity, we must take into consideration all these factors connected with speaking activities. But the sentences, and the signs (e.g., words) occurring in them, are sometimes involved in still another relation. A sign or expression may concern or designate or describe something, or, rather, he who uses the expression may intend to refer to something by it, e.g., to an object or a property or a state of affairs; this we call the *designatum* of the expression. (For the moment, no exact definition for 'designatum' is intended; this word is merely to serve as a convenient, common term for different cases—objects, properties, etc.—whose fundamental differences in other respects are not hereby denied.) Thus, three components have to be distinguished in a situation where language is used. We see these in the following example: (1) the action, state, and environment of a man who speaks or hears, say, the German word 'blau'; (2) the word 'blau' as an element of the German language (meant here as a specified acoustic [or visual] design which is the common property of the many sounds produced at different times, which may be called the tokens of that design); (3) a certain property of things, viz., the color blue, to which this man—and German-speaking people in general—intends to refer (one usually says, "The man means the color by the word", or "The word means the color for these people", or ". . . . within this language").

The complete theory of language has to study all these three components. We shall call *pragmatics* the field of all those investigations which take into consideration the first component, whether it be alone or in combination with the other components. Other inquiries are made in abstraction from the speaker and deal only with the expressions of the language and their relation to their designata. The field of these studies is called *semantics*. Finally, one may abstract even from the designata and restrict the investigation to formal properties—in a sense soon to be explained—of the expressions and relations among them. This field is called *logical syntax*. The distinction between the three fields will become more clear in our subsequent discussions.

That an investigation of language has to take into consideration all the three factors mentioned was in recent times made clear and emphasized especially by C. S. Peirce, by Ogden and Richards, and by Morris (see Vol. I, No. 2). Morris made it the basis for the three fields into which he divides semiotic (i.e., the general theory of signs), namely, pragmatics, semantics, and syntactics. Our division is in agreement with his in its chief features. For general questions concerning language and its use compare also Bloomfield, Volume I, No. 4.

3. Pragmatics of Language B

In order to make clear the nature of the three fields and the differences between them, we shall analyze an example of a language. We choose a fictitious language B, very poor and very simple in its structure, in order to get simple systems of semantical and syntactical rules.

Whenever an investigation is made about a language, we call this language the *object-language* of the investigation, and the language in which the results of the investigation are formulated the *metalanguage*. Sometimes object-language and meta-language are the same, e.g., when we speak in English about English. The theory concerning the object-language which is formulated in the metalanguage is sometimes called metatheory. Its three branches are the pragmatics, the semantics, and the syntax of the language in question. In what follows, B is our object-language, English our metalanguage.

Suppose we find a group of people speaking a language B which we do not understand; nor do they understand ours. After some observation, we discover which words the people use, in which forms of sentences they use them, what these words and sentences are about, on what occasions they are used, what activities are connected with them, etc. Thus we may have obtained the following results, numbered here for later reference.

Pragm. 1.—Whenever the people utter a sentence of the form '. . . ist kalt', where '. . .' is the name of a thing, they intend to assert that the thing in question is cold.

Pragm. 2a.—A certain lake in that country, which has no name in English, is usually called 'titisee'. When using this name, the people often think of plenty of fish and good meals.

Pragm. 2b.—On certain holidays the lake is called 'rumber';

when using this name, the people often think—even during good weather—of the dangers of storm on the lake.

Pragm. 3.—The word 'nicht' is used in sentences of the form 'nicht . . .', where '. . .' is a sentence. If the sentence '. . .' serves to express the assertion that such and such is the case, the whole sentence 'nicht . . .' is acknowledged as a correct assertion if such and such is not the case.

In this way we slowly learn the designata and mode of use of all the words and expressions, especially the sentences; we find out both the cause and the effect of their utterance. We may study the preferences of different social groups, age groups, or geographical groups in the choice of expressions. We investigate the role of the language in various social relations, etc.

The pragmatics of language B consists of all these and similar investigations. Pragmatical observations are the basis of all linguistic research. We see that pragmatics is an empirical discipline dealing with a special kind of human behavior and making use of the results of different branches of science (principally social science, but also physics, biology, and psychology).

4. Semantical Systems

We now proceed to restrict our attention to a special aspect of the facts concerning the language B which we have found by observations of the speaking activities within the group who speak that language. We study the relations between the expressions of B and their designata. On the basis of those facts we are going to lay down a system of rules establishing those relations. We call them *semantical rules*. These rules are not unambiguously determined by the facts. Suppose we have found that the word 'mond' of B was used in 98 per cent of the cases for the moon and in 2 per cent for a certain lantern. Now it is a matter of our decision whether we construct the rules in such a way that both the moon and the lantern are designata of 'mond' or only the moon. If we choose the first, the use of 'mond' in those 2 per cent of cases was right—with respect to our rules; if we choose the second, it was wrong. The facts do not determine whether the use of a certain expression is right or wrong but only how often it occurs and how often it leads to the effect intended, and the like. A question of right or wrong must always refer to a system of rules. Strictly speaking, the rules which we shall lay down are not rules of the factually given language B; they rather constitute a language system corresponding to B which we will call the *semantical system B-S*. The language B belongs to the world of facts; it has many properties, some of which we have found, while others are unknown to us. The language system B-S, on the other hand, is something constructed by us; it has all and only those properties which we establish by the rules. Nevertheless, we construct B-S not arbitrarily but with regard to the facts about B. Then we may make the empirical statement that the language B is to a certain degree in accordance with the system B-S. The previously mentioned pragmatical facts are the basis—in the sense explained—of some of the rules to be given later (Pragm. 1 for SD 2*a* and SL 1, Pragm. 2*a,b* for SD 1*a*, Pragm. 3 for SL 2).

We call the elements of a semantical system *signs;* they may be words or special symbols like '0', '+', etc. A sequence consisting of one or several signs is called an *expression*. As signs of the system B-S we take the words which we have found by our observations to be words of B or, rather, only those words which we decide to accept as "correct." We divide the signs of B-S—and, in an analogous way, those of any other semantical system—into two classes: *descriptive* and *logical* signs. As descriptive signs we take those which designate things or properties of things (in a more comprehensive system we should classify here also the relations among things, functions of things, etc.). The other signs are taken as logical signs: they serve chiefly for connecting descriptive signs in the construction of sentences but do not themselves designate things, properties of things, etc. Logical signs are, e.g., those corresponding to English words like 'is', 'are', 'not', 'and', 'or', 'if', 'any', 'some', 'every', 'all'. These unprecise explanations will suffice here. Our later discussions will show some of the differentiae of the two classes of signs.

Semantics as an exact discipline is quite new; we owe it to the very fertile school of contemporary Polish logicians. After some of this group, especially Lesniewski and Ajdukiewicz, had discussed semantical questions, Tarski, in his treatise on truth, made the first comprehensive systematic investigation in this field, giving rise to very important results.

5. Rules of the Semantical System B-S

In order to show how semantical rules are to be formulated and how they serve to determine truth conditions and thereby give an interpretation of the sentences, we are going to construct the semantical rules for the system B-S. As preliminary steps for this construction we make a classification of the signs and lay down rules of formation. Each class is defined by an enumeration of the signs belonging to it. The signs of B-S are divided into descriptive and logical signs. The descriptive signs of B-S are divided into names and predicates. Names are the words 'titisee', 'rumber', 'mond', etc. (here a complete list of the names has to be given). Predicates are the words 'kalt', 'blau', 'rot', etc. The logical signs are divided into logical constants ('ist', 'nicht', 'wenn', 'so', 'fuer', 'jedes') and variables ('x', 'y', etc.). For the general description of forms of expressions we shall use blanks like '. . .', '- - -', etc. They are not themselves signs of B-S but have to be replaced by expressions of B-S. If nothing else is said, a blank stands for any expression of B-S. A blank with a subscript 'n', 'p', 's', or 'v' (e.g., '. . .$_n$') stands for a name, a predicate, a sentence, or a variable, respectively. If the same blank occurs several times within a rule or a statement, it stands at all places for the same expression.

The rules of formation determine how sentences may be constructed out of the various kinds of signs.

Rules of formation.—An expression of B-S is called a *sentence* (in the semantical sense) or a *proposition* of B-S, if and only if it has one of the following forms, F 1–4. F 1: '. . .$_n$ ist - - -$_p$' (e.g., 'mond ist blau'); F 2: 'nicht. . .$_s$' (e.g., 'nicht mond ist blau'); F 3: 'wenn . . .$_s$, so - - -$_s$' (e.g., 'wenn titisee ist rot, so mond ist kalt'); F 4: 'fuer jedes . . .$_v$, - . . .-', where '- . . .-' stands for an expression which is formed out of a sentence not containing a variable by replacing one or several names by the variable

'. .$_v$' (e.g., 'fuer jedes x, x ist blau'; 'fuer jedes y, wenn y ist blau, so y ist kalt'). The partial sentence in a sentence of the form F 2 and the two partial sentences in a sentence of the form F 3 (indicated above by blanks) are called *components* of the whole sentence. In order to indicate the components of a sentence in case they are themselves compound, commas and square brackets are used when necessary.

Rules B-SD. Designata of descriptive signs:

SD 1. The *names* designate things, and especially
   a) each of the thing-names 'titisee' and 'rumber' designates the lake at such and such a longitude and latitude.
   b) 'mond' designates the moon.
   Etc. [Here is to be given a complete list of rules for all the names of B-S.]

SD 2. The *predicates* designate properties of things, and especially
   a) 'kalt' designates the property of being cold.
   b) 'blau' designates the property of being blue.
   c) 'rot' designates the property of being red.
   Etc. [for all predicates].

Rules B-SL. Truth conditions for the sentences of B-S. These rules involve the *logical signs*. We call them the L-semantical rules of B-S.

SL 1. 'ist', form F 1. A sentence of the form '. . .$_n$ ist - - -$_p$' is true if and only if the thing designated by '. . .$_n$' has the property designated by '- - -$_p$'.

SL 2. 'nicht', form F 2. A sentence of the form 'nicht . . .$_s$' is true if and only if the sentence '. . .$_s$' is not true.

SL 3. 'wenn' and 'so', form F 3. A sentence of the form 'wenn . . .$_s$, so - - -$_s$' is true if and only if '. . .$_s$' is not true or '- - -$_s$' is true.

SL 4. 'fuer jedes', form F 4. A sentence of the form 'fuer jedes . .$_v$, - . . . -', where '- . . . -' is an expression formed out of a sentence by replacing one or several names by the variable '. .$_v$', is true if and only if all sentences of the following kind are true: namely, those sentences constructed out of the expression '- . . -' by replacing the variable '. .ᵥ' at all places where it occurs within that expression by a name, the same for all places; here names of any things may be taken, even of those for which there is no name in the list of names in B-S. (Example: The sentence 'fuer jedes *x*, *x* ist blau' is true if and only if every sentence of the form '. . .ₙ ist blau' is true; hence, according to SL 1, if and only if everything is blue.)

The rule SL 1, in combination with SD, provides direct truth conditions for the sentences of the simplest form; direct, since the rule does not refer to the truth of other sentences. SL 2–4 provide indirect truth conditions for the compound sentences by referring to other sentences and finally back to sentences of the simplest form. Hence the rules B-SD and SL together give a general definition of '*true* in B-S' though not in explicit form. (It would be possible, although in a rather complicated form, to formulate an explicit definition of 'true in B-S' on the basis of the rules given.) A sentence of B-S which is not true in B-S is called *false* in B-S.

If a sentence of B-S is given, one can easily construct, with the help of the given rules, a direct *truth-criterion* for it, i.e., a necessary and sufficient condition for its truth, in such a way that in the formulation of this condition no reference is made to the truth of other sentences. Since to know the truth conditions of a sentence is to know what is asserted by it, the given semantical rules determine for every sentence of B-S what it asserts—in usual terms, its "meaning"—or, in other words, how it is to be translated into English.

Examples: (1) The sentence 'mond ist blau' is true if and only if the moon is blue. (2) The sentence 'fuer jedes *x*, wenn *x* ist blau, so *x* ist kalt' is true if and only if every thing—not only those having a name in B-S—either is not blue or is cold; in other words, if all blue things are cold. Hence, this sentence asserts that all blue things are cold; it is to be translated into the English sentence 'all blue things are cold'.

Therefore, we shall say that we *understand* a language system, or a sign, or an expression, or a sentence in a language system, if we know the semantical rules of the system. We shall also say that the semantical rules give an *interpretation* of the language system.

We have formulated the semantical rules of the descriptive signs by stating their designata, for the logical signs by stating truth conditions for the sentences constructed with their help. We may mention here two other ways of formulating them which are often used in the practice of linguistics and logic. The first consists in giving *translations* for the signs and, if necessary, for the complex expressions and sentences, as it is done in a dictionary. The second way consists in stating *designata* throughout, not only for the descriptive signs as in SD, but also for expressions containing the logical signs, corresponding to SL. Example (corresponding to SL 1): A sentence of the form '. . .$_n$ ist - - -$_p$' designates (the state of affairs) that the thing designated by '. . .$_n$' has the property designated by '- - -$_p$'.

6. Some Terms of Semantics

We shall define some more terms which belong to the metalanguage and, moreover, to the semantical part of the metalanguage (as is seen from the fact that the definitions refer to the semantical rules). Any semantical term is relative to a semantical system and must, in strict formulation, be accompanied by a reference to that system. In practice the reference may often be omitted without ambiguity (thus we say, e.g., simply 'synonymous' instead of 'synonymous in B-S').

Two expressions are said to be semantically synonymous, or briefly, *synonymous*, with each other in a semantical system S if they have the same designatum by virtue of the rules of S. Hence, according to SD 1a, the signs 'titisee' and 'rumber' are semantically synonymous with one another in B-S. They are, however, not what we might call pragmatically synonymous in B, as is shown by Pragm. 2a,b. Since the transition from pragmatics to semantics is an abstraction, some properties drop out of consideration and hence some distinctions disappear. Because of the semantical synonymity of the names mentioned, the sentences 'titisee ist kalt' and 'rumber ist kalt' are also semantically synonymous. These two sentences have the same truth conditions, although different pragmatical conditions of application. Suppose that the lake is cold and hence the sentence 'titisee ist kalt' is true. Then the sentence 'rumber is kalt' is also true, even if sinfully spoken on a working day. If this happened by mistake, people would tell the speaker that he is right in his belief but that he ought to formulate it—i.e., the same belief—in another way.

We shall apply the semantical terms to be defined not only to sentences but also to classes of sentences. In what follows we shall use 'S_1', 'S_2', etc., for sentences; 'C_1', 'C_2', etc., for classes of sentences; 'T_1', 'T_2', etc., stand both for sentences and for classes of sentences. (These 'S' and 'C' with subscripts have nothing to do with the same letters without subscripts, which we use for semantical systems and calculi, e.g., 'B-S' and 'B-C'.) We understand the assertion of a class of sentences C_1 as a simultaneous assertion of all the sentences belonging to C_1; therefore, we make the following definition: a *class* of sentences C_1 is called *true* if all sentences of C_1 are true; false, if at least one of them is false. T_1 and T_2 (i.e., two sentences, or two classes of sentences, or one sentence and one class) are called *equivalent* with each other, if either both are true or both are false. T_2 is called an *implicate* of T_1, if T_1 is false or T_2 is true. T_1 is said to *exclude* T_2 if not both are true.

7. L-Semantical Terms

Let us compare the following two sentences: 'Australia is large' (S_1) and 'Australia is large or Australia is not large' (S_2). We see that they have a quite different character; let us try to give an exact account of their difference. We learn S_1 in geography but S_2 in logic. In order to find out for each of these sentences whether it is true or false, we must, of course, first understand the language to which it belongs. Then, for S_1 we have to know, in addition, some facts about the thing whose name occurs in it, i.e., Australia. Such is not the case for S_2. Whether Australia is large or small does not matter here; just by understanding S_2 we become aware that it must be right. If we agree to use the same term 'true' in both cases, we may express their difference by saying that S_1 is factually (or empirically) true while S_2 is logically true. These unprecise explanations can easily be transformed into precise definitions by replacing the former reference to understanding by a reference to semantical rules. We call a sentence of a semantical system S (logically true or) *L-true* if it is true in such a way that the semantical rules of S suffice for establishing its truth. We call a sentence (logically false or) *L-false* if it is false in such a way that the semantical rules suffice for finding that it is false. The two terms just defined and all other terms defined on their basis we call *L-semantical terms*. If a sentence is either L-true or L-false, it is called *L-determinate*, otherwise (L-indeterminate or) *factual*. (The terms 'L-true', 'L-false', and 'factual' correspond to the terms 'analytic', 'contradictory', and 'synthetic', as they are used in traditional terminology, usually without exact definitions.) If a factual sentence is true, it is called (factually true or) *F-true;* if it is false, (factually false or) *F-false*. Every sentence which contains only logical signs is L-determinate. This is one of the chief characteristics distinguishing logical from descriptive signs. (Example: 'For every object x and every property F, if x is an F then x is an F' is L-true. There are no sentences of this kind in the system B-S.)

Classification of sentences of a semantical system:

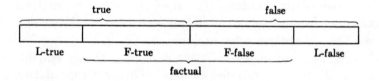

Examples of sentences in B-S: (1) We found earlier (§ 5) that the sentence 'mond ist blau' (S_1) is true in B-S if and only if the moon is blue. Hence, in order to find out whether S_1 is true or false, not only must we know the rules of B-S but we have to make observations of the moon. Hence S_1 is not L-determinate but factual. (2) Let us analyze the sentence 'wenn mond ist blau, so mond is blau' (S_2). According to rule SL 3, a 'wenn-so' sentence is true if its first component is not true or its second component is true. Now, if S_1 is true, the second component of S_2 is true, and hence S_2 is true; and if S_1 is not true, then the first component of S_2 is not true, and hence S_2 is again true. Thus S_2 is true in any case, independently of the facts concerning the moon; it is true merely in virtue of rule SL 3. Therefore S_2 is L-true. (3) The sentence 'nicht, wenn mond ist blau, so mond ist blau' (S_3) has S_2 as its component; and we found S_2 to be true on the basis of SL 3. Therefore, according to *SL 2*, S_3 is not true but false. And, moreover, it is false not because some fact happens to be the case but merely by virtue of the rules SL 3 and 2. Hence, S_3 is L-false.

Terminological remark.—The use of the word 'true' in everyday language and in philosophy is restricted by some to factual sentences, while some others use it in a wider sense, including analytic sentences. We adopted here the wider use; it is more customary in modern logic (e.g., 'truth function', 'truth-value-table'), and it turns out to be much more convenient. Otherwise, we should always have to say in the semantical rules and in most of the semantical theorems 'true or analytic' instead of 'true'. Semantical rules stating truth-conditions in the sense of 'F-true' would become very complicated and indeed indefinite.

The definitions given can easily be transferred to classes of sentences. C_1 is called L-true if it is possible to find out that C_1 is true with the help of the semantical rules alone, hence if all sentences of C_1 are L-true. C_1 is called L-false if it is possible to find out with the help of the semantical rules that C_1 is false, i.e., that at least one sentence of C_1 is false (in this case, however, all sentences of C_1 may be factual). If C_1 is either L-true or L-false, it is called L-determinate, otherwise factual.

If the semantical rules suffice to show that T_2 is an implicate of T_1, we call T_2 an *L-implicate* of T_1. This relation of L-implication is one of the fundamental concepts in logical analysis of language. The criterion for it can also be formulated in this way: the semantical rules exclude the possibility of T_1 being true and T_2 false; or in this way: according to the semantical rules, if T_1 is true, T_2 must be true. This last formulation of the criterion shows that L-implication, as defined here, is essentially the same as what is usually called logical consequence or deducibility or strict implication or entailment, although the form of the definitions of these terms may be different. Our definition is a semantical one as it refers to the semantical rules. Later we shall discuss the possibility of defining a corresponding syntactical term.

Examples: (1) 'mond ist rot' (S_1); 'wenn mond ist rot, so titisee ist kalt' (S_2); 'titisee ist kalt' (S_3). We shall see that S_3 is an L-implicate of the class C_1 consisting of S_1 and S_2. According to the definition of 'implicate' (§ 6), if S_3 is true, S_3 is an implicate of C_1. The same holds if S_1 is false because C_1 is then also false. The only remaining case is that S_1 is true and S_3 is false. In this case, according to rule SL 3 (§ 5), S_2 is false and, hence, C_1 is false too, and S_3 is an implicate of C_1. Thus we have found, without examining the facts described by the sentences, and merely by referring to the semantical rules, that S_3 is an implicate of C_1. Therefore, S_3 is an L-implicate of C_1. (2) 'fuer jedes x, x ist blau' (S_4); 'mond ist blau' (S_5). We shall see that S_5 is an L-implicate of S_4. If S_5 is true, S_5 is an implicate of S_4. And if S_5 is not true, then according to SL 4 (§ 5), S_4 is not true, and, hence, S_5 is again an implicate of S_4. We found this result by merely referring to a semantical rule. Therefore, S_5 is an L-implicate of S_4.

T_1 and T_2 are said to be *L-equivalent* if the semantical rules suffice to establish their equivalence, in other words, if T_1 and T_2 are L-implicates of each other. L-equivalent sentences have the same truth conditions; therefore, they say the same thing, although the formulations may be quite different.

Example: 'mond ist kalt' (S_1); 'nicht, mond ist kalt' (S_2); 'nicht, nicht, mond ist kalt' (S_3). These sentences are factual; the semantical rules do not suffice for finding out their truth or falsity. But they suffice for showing that S_1 and S_3 are equivalent. If S_1 is true, S_2 is, according to SL 2 (§ 5), false, and hence S_3 true. Therefore, in this case, S_1 and S_3 are equivalent. And, if S_1 is false, then S_2 is true and S_3 is false; hence, S_1 and S_3 are again equivalent. Thus, on the basis of the semantical rules, S_1 and S_3 cannot be other than equivalent. Therefore they are L-equivalent.

If S_1 is an L-true sentence, then the truth of S_1 can be established without any regard to the facts, e.g., to the properties of the things whose names occur in S_1. Therefore, S_1 does not convey any information about facts; this is sometimes formulated by saying that an L-true sentence has no factual content. Suppose S_2 to be an L-implicate of the class of sentences C_1. Then S_2 is an implicate of C_1, and hence, if the sentences of C_1 are true, S_2 is also true; and, moreover, this relation between C_1 and S_2 can be found to hold without taking into account any facts. Therefore, S_2 does not furnish any new information concerning facts that were not already given by C_1. This is sometimes expressed by saying that logical deduction does not increase the factual content of the premises. The two characteristics just explained of L-truth and L-implication (which have been especially emphasized by Wittgenstein) are very important for a clear understanding of the relation between logic and empirical knowledge. We shall see later that they hold also for mathematical theorems and mathematical deductions even if applied in empirical science (§ 19).

8. Logical Syntax

We distinguished three factors in the functioning of language: the activities of the speaking and listening persons, the designata, and the expressions of the language. We abstracted from the first factor and thereby came from pragmatics to semantics. Now we shall abstract from the second factor also and thus proceed from semantics to syntax. We shall take into consideration only the expressions, leaving aside the objects, properties, states of affairs, or whatever may be designated by the expressions. The relation of designation will be disregarded entirely. As this relation is the basis of the whole semantical system, it might seem as if nothing would be left. But we shall soon see that this is not the case.

A definition of a term in the metalanguage is called *formal* if it refers only to the expressions of the object-language (or, more exactly, to the kinds of signs and the order in which they occur in the expressions) but not to any extralinguistic objects and especially not to the designata of the descriptive signs of the object-language. A term defined by a formal definition is also called formal, as are questions, proofs, investigations, etc., in which only formal terms occur. We call the formal theory of an object-language, formulated in the metalanguage, the *syntax* of the object-language (or the logical syntax, whenever it seems necessary to distinguish this theory from that part of linguistics which is known as syntax but which usually is not restricted to formal terms). A formal definition, term, analysis, etc., is then also called syntactical.

The definitions of all semantical terms refer directly or indirectly to designata. But some of these terms—e.g., 'true', 'L-true', 'L-implicate'—are attributed not to designata but only to expressions; they designate properties of, or relations between, expressions. Now our question is whether it is possible to define within syntax, i.e., in a formal way, terms which correspond more or less to those semantical terms, i.e., whose extensions coincide partly or completely with theirs. The development of syntax—chiefly in modern symbolic logic—has led to an affirmative answer to that question. Especially is the possibility of defining in a formal way terms which completely correspond to 'L-true' and 'L-implicate' of fundamental importance. This shows that logical deduction can be completely formalized.

A *syntactical system* or *calculus* (sometimes also called a formal deductive system or a formal system) is a system of formal rules which determine certain formal properties and relations of sentences, especially for the purpose of formal deduction. The simplest procedure for the construction of a calculus consists in laying down some sentences as primitive sentences (sometimes called postulates or axioms) and some rules of inference. The primitive sentences and rules of inference are used for two purposes, for the construction of proofs and of derivations. We shall call the sentences to which the proofs lead *C-true* sentences (they are often called provable or proved sentences or theorems of the calculus). A derivation leads from any not necessarily C-true sentences, called the premisses, to a sentence, called the conclusion. We shall call the conclusion a *C-implicate* of the class of premisses (it is sometimes called derivable or derived or [formally] deducible or deduced from the premisses or a [formal] consequence of the premisses). A calculus may (but usually does not) also contain rules which determine certain sentences as *C-false*. If the rules of a calculus determine some sentence as both C-true and C-false, the calculus is called *inconsistent;* otherwise *consistent*. (If, as is usually done, no rules for 'C-false' are given, the calculus cannot be inconsistent.) In order to explain this procedure, we shall construct the calculus B-C as an example.

Logical syntax has chiefly grown out of two roots, one being formal logic, founded by Aristotle, the other the axiomatic method, initiated by Euclid. The general idea of operations with calculi goes back to Leibniz; since the middle of the last century it has been developed in the systems of symbolic logic into a comprehensive discipline. Among the founders of symbolic logic, or logistic, Boole (1854) is especially to be mentioned. More comprehensive systems (including the higher functional calculus [see § 14]) were created by Schroeder (1890), Frege (1893), Peano (1895), and Whitehead and Russell (1910). Frege was the first to formulate explicitly and to fulfil strictly the requirement of formality, i.e., of a formulation of rules of logic without any reference to designata. Hilbert considerably developed the axiomatic method, in its application both to geometry (see § 21) and to classical mathematics (see §§ 18 and 20).

9. The Calculus B-C

While the sentences of a semantical system are interpreted, assert something, and therefore are either true or false, within a calculus the sentences are looked at from a purely formal point of view. In order to emphasize this distinction, we sometimes call sentences as elements of a semantical system *propositions* and as elements of a calculus *formulas*.

We constructed earlier a semantical system B-S on the basis of the language B, but not, as we have seen, uniquely determined by B. Analogously, we shall now construct a calculus B-C on the basis of B. As preliminary steps for the construction of the syntactical rules proper, which we shall then call rules of transformation, we have to make a *classification* of the signs of B-C and to lay down *syntactical rules of formation* F$_C$ 1-4. But they correspond exactly to the classification and the rules of formation F 1-4 of B-S (§ 5); these rules were already formal. Therefore we shall not write them down again.

Calculus B-C. Rules of Transformation:

PS.   A sentence of B-C is called a *primitive sentence* of B-C, if it has one of the following forms, PS 1-4:

PS 1. 'wenn . . . , so [wenn nicht . . . , so - - -]'.

PS 2. 'wenn [wenn nicht . . . , so . . .], so . . .'.

PS 3. 'wenn [wenn . . . , so - - -], so [wenn [wenn - - -, so . - . .-], so [wenn . . . , so . - . -]]'.

PS 4. 'wenn [fuer jedes . . , - . . . -], so - . - . -'; here '. .' is a variable, '- . - . -' is a sentence which does not contain 'fuer jedes' but contains a name '. - .' one or several times, and '- . . .-' is an expression constructed out of '- . . . -' by replacing '. - .' at one or several (not necessarily all) places by the variable '. .'. (Examples: [1] 'wenn [fuer jedes x, x ist rot], so mond ist rot'; [2] see sentence (3) in the first example of a derivation, at the end of this section.)

R. Rules of Inference: The relation of direct derivability holds if and only if one of the following conditions is fulfilled.

R 1. Rule of Implication: From 'wenn ..., so - - -' and '...', '- - -' is directly derivable in B-C.

R 2. Rule of Synonymity: The words 'titisee' and 'rumber' may be exchanged at any place (i.e., if S_2 is constructed out of S_1 by replacing one of those words at one place by the other one, then S_2 is directly derivable from S_1 in B-C).

· A *proof* in B-C is a sequence of sentences of B-C such that each of them is either a primitive sentence or directly derivable from one or two sentences preceding it in the sequence. A sentence S_1 of B-C is called *provable* in B-C if it is the last sentence of a proof in B-C. A sentence of B-C is called *C-true* in B-C if and only if it is provable in B-C; a sentence '...' is called *C-false* in B-C if and only if 'nicht ...' is provable in B-C. (For B-C, provability and C-truth coincide, and likewise derivability and C-implication; for other calculi, this is in general not the case, as we shall see.)

A *derivation* in B-C with a class C_1 of premises is a sequence of sentences of B-C such that each of them is either a sentence of C_1 or a primitive sentence or directly derivable from one or two sentences preceding it in the sequence. The last sentence of a derivation is called its *conclusion*. S_2 is called *derivable* from C_1 and also a *C-implicate* of C_1 if it is the conclusion of a derivation with the class of premises C_1.

Both the rules of formation and the rules of transformation of B-C do not in any way refer to designata; they are strictly formal. Nevertheless, they have been chosen with regard to B-S in such a way that the extension of the terms 'C-true', 'C-false', and 'C-implicate' in B-C coincides with that of 'L-true', 'L-false', and 'L-implicate', respectively, in B-S. There are an infinite number of other possible choices of primitive sentences and rules of inference which would lead to the same result. This result gives the practical justification for our choice of the rules of B-C. A calculus in itself needs no justification; this point will be discussed later.

The calculus B-C corresponds to a restricted form of the so-called lower functional calculus, as constructed by Hilbert and Bernays. PS 1–3 and R 1 correspond to the so-called sentential calculus. That the lower functional calculus is complete, i.e., that it exhausts the extension of L-truth and L-implication, has been shown by Gödel.

Example of a proof in B-C. If in the following sequence the blank '. .' is always replaced by the same sentence, e.g., 'titisee ist blau', the sequence fulfils the conditions—as shown by the remarks on the left side—and therefore is a proof. Hence any sentence of the form 'wenn ..., so ...' is provable and C-true in B-C, e.g., 'wenn titisee ist blau, so titisee ist blau'.

PS 1	wenn ..., so [wenn nicht ..., so ...]	(1)
PS 2	wenn [wenn nicht ..., so ...], so ...	(2)
PS 3	wenn [wenn ..., so.[wenn nicht ..., so ...]],	
	so [wenn [wenn [wenn nicht ..., so ...], so ...],	
	so [wenn ..., so ...]]	(3)

(here, 'wenn nicht ..., so ...' has been taken for '- - -', and '...' for '. - .-')

(1)(3) R 1	wenn [wenn [wenn nicht ..., so ...], so ...],	
	so [wenn ..., so ...]	(4)
(2)(4) R 1	wenn ..., so ...	(5)

First example of a derivation in B-C:

Premisses {titisee ist blau		(1)
{fuer jedes x, [wenn x ist blau, so x ist kalt]		(2)
PS 4	wenn [fuer jedes x, [wenn x ist blau, so x ist kalt]], so [wenn titisee ist blau, so titisee ist kalt]	(3)
(2)(3) R 1	wenn titisee ist blau, so titisee ist kalt	(4)
(1)(4) R 1	*Conclusion:* titisee ist kalt	(5)

If we interpret these sentences as in B-S, (1) says that a certain object is blue, (2) says that all blue things are cold (see example [2] at the end of § 5), (5) says that that object is cold. Here, however, the conclusion is derived from the premisses in a formal way, i.e., without making use of an interpretation.

Second example of a derivation in B-C:

Premisses {wenn mond ist blau, so mond ist kalt		(1)
{nicht mond ist kalt		(2)
Provable:	wenn [wenn mond ist blau, so mond ist kalt], so [wenn nicht mond ist kalt, so nicht mond ist blau]	(3)

(1)(3) R 1 wenn nicht mond ist k. it, so nicht mond ist blau   (4)
(2)(4) R 1 *Conclusion:* nicht mono ist blau   (5)

(3) is a provable sentence. To save space, we do not give its proof here. Suppose that the proof of (3) has been constructed earlier, then the example shows how its result can be used in a derivation. According to the definitions previously given for 'proof' and 'derivation', any proof may also occur as a part of a derivation. If this happens, we can abbreviate the derivation; we write in the derivation not all the sentences of the proof, whose last sentence we intend to use, but only this one sentence, as we have done in the example given with sentence (3). In this way a sentence which has been proved once can be used in derivations again and again. Later, in the discussion of the application of calculi in empirical science we shall come back to this application of proved sentences in derivations (§ 19).

II. Calculus and Interpretation

10. Calculus and Semantical System

We shall investigate the relations which may hold between a calculus and a semantical system. Sometimes we shall use as examples the calculus B-C and the semantical system B-S as discussed before. Suppose a calculus is given—it may be designated by 'Z-C' or briefly 'C'—and a semantical system—designated by 'Z-S' or 'S'. We call S an *interpretation* of C if the rules of S determine truth criteria for all sentences of C; in other words, if to every formula of C there is a corresponding proposition of S; the converse is not required.

Suppose S fulfils the following condition: for any T_1, T_2, T_3, and T_4, if T_2 is a C-implicate of T_1 in C, T_2 is an implicate of T_1 in S; if T_3 is C-true in C, it is true in S; if T_4 is C-false in C, it is false in S. If an interpretation S of C fulfils the condition stated, we call it a *true interpretation* of C; otherwise a *false interpretation*. If the semantical rules suffice to show that S is a true interpretation of C, then we call S an *L-true interpretation* of C. In this case C-implication becomes L-implication; every C-true sentence becomes L-true, and every C-false sentence becomes L-false. If, on the other hand, these semantical rules suffice to show that S is a false interpretation, we call S an *L-false interpretation*. If S is an interpretation but neither an

L-true nor an L-false interpretation of C, we call S a *factual interpretation* of C. In this case, in order to find out whether the interpretation is true, we have to find out whether some factual sentences are true; for this task we have to carry out empirical investigations about facts. An interpretation S of C is called a *logical interpretation* if all sentences of C become logical sentences of S (i.e., sentences containing logical signs only), otherwise a *descriptive interpretation*. A logical interpretation is always L-determinate. Applying these definitions to the system of our former example: B-S is a true and, moreover, L-true, and descriptive interpretation of B-C.

The class of the sentences which are C-true in C is, interpreted by S, a class of assertions; we call it the *theory correlated* to C by S. If the interpretation is true, L-true or logical, respectively, the correlated theory is likewise true, L-true or logical, respectively; the converse does not hold generally.

Previously we had a semantical system B-S and then constructed a calculus B-C "in accordance with" B-S. What was meant by this can now be formulated: we intended to construct B-C in such a way that B-S is a true interpretation of B-C. It is easy to see that for any given semantical system S it is possible to construct a calculus C of that kind. All we have to do is to select partial domains, as small as we wish, of the extensions of 'implicate in S', 'true in S', and 'false in S' (usually the null class), and then lay down formal definitions of 'C-implicate', 'C-true', and possibly 'C-false', in such a way that their extensions correspond to these partial domains. On the other hand, it is an important problem whether it is possible to construct for a given system S a calculus C such that C is not only in accordance with S, in the sense explained, but that the extensions of 'C-implicate', 'C-true', and (if defined at all) 'C-false' coincide with those of 'L-implicate', 'L-true', and possibly 'L-false,' respectively. If this is the case, we call C an *L-exhaustive calculus* with respect to S. Thus B-C is L-exhaustive with respect to B-S. (We do not define a term for the case that the extensions of 'C-implicate', 'C-true', and 'C-false' coincide with those of 'implicate', 'true', and 'false' because that would be impossible for any somewhat richer language system, e.g., for any language system of a branch of science.)

In order to answer the question of the possibility of an L-exhaustive calculus, we have to distinguish two fundamentally different kinds of rules of transformation, which we call finite and transfinite rules. By *finite rules* we understand those of the customary kind: primitive sentences and rules of inference each of which refers to a finite number of premises (in most cases one or two). Almost all rules used by logicians up to the present time are finite. Finite rules are applied in the construction of proofs and derivations of the usual kind, which are finite sequences of sentences, as we have seen in the examples in B-C. A rule of transformation is called *transfinite* if it refers to an infinite number of premises. Because of this number being infinite, a transfinite rule cannot be used within a proof or derivation; a procedure of deduction of an entirely new kind is necessary. We call a calculus finite if all its rules of transformation are finite, otherwise transfinite. It may be remarked that some logicians reject transfinite rules.

We shall make the following terminological distinction: the terms 'C-implicate' and 'C-true' are applied generally with respect both to finite and to transfinite calculi. On the other hand, we shall restrict the corresponding terms 'derivable' and 'provable' to finite calculi. Thus we call T_2 a C-implicate of T_1 in C, if it is possible to obtain T_2 from the premises T_1 by a procedure of deduction of any kind in C; and we call T_3 C-true if it is possible to obtain T_3 by a procedure of deduction without premises. If C is a finite calculus— as, e.g., B-C—the deduction takes the form of a finite sequence of sentences, either a derivation or a proof. In this case T_2 is called, moreover, derivable from T_1, and T_3 is called, moreover, provable.

Now we come back to the problem whether it is possible to construct for a given semantical system S an L-exhaustive calculus C. The answer can now be formulated (but not proved here). The answer depends upon the degree of complexity of S; more precisely, it depends upon whether there are in S a sentence S_2 and an infinite class of sentences C_1 such that S_2 is an L-implicate of C_1 but not an L-implicate of any finite subclass of C_1. (Example. S contains a name for every object of an infinite domain: 'a_1', 'a_2', 'a_3', etc. 'P' is a descriptive predicate. C_1 is the [infinite] class of all sentences of the form '. . . is a P' where '. . .' is one of the object names. S_2 is the sentence 'for every x, x is a P'.) If this is not the case, then there is a finite L-exhaustive calculus C. If, however, it is the case, an L-exhaustive calculus C can be constructed if and only if transfinite rules are admitted. For, because C_1 is infinite, S_2 cannot be derivable from C_1. If we decide in a given case to admit transfinite rules, we have to accept the complications and methodological difficulties connected with them. It was first shown by Gödel that a calculus of the ordinary kind (in our terminology, a finite calculus) cannot be constructed for the whole of arithmetic.

11. On the Construction of a Language System

We found earlier that the pragmatical description of a language gives some suggestions for the construction of a corresponding semantical system without, however, determining it. Therefore, there is a certain amount of freedom for the selection and formulation of the semantical rules. Again, if a semantical system S is given and a calculus C is to be constructed in accordance with S, we are bound in some respects and free in others. The rules of formation of C are given by S. And in the construction of the rules of transformation we are restricted by the condition that C must be such that S is a true interpretation of C, as discussed before. But this still leaves some range of choice. We may, for instance, decide that the class of C-true sentences is to be only a proper subclass of the class of L-true sentences, or that it is to coincide with that class (as we did in constructing B-C), or that it is to go beyond that class and comprehend some factual sentences, e.g., some physical laws. When the extensions of 'C-true' and 'C-implicate' are decided, there is still some possibility of choice in the construction of the rules, e.g., primitive sentences and rules of inference, leading to those extensions. This choice, however, is not of essential importance, as it concerns more the form of presentation than the result.

If we are concerned with a historically given language, the pragmatical description comes first, and then we may go by abstraction to semantics and (either from semantics or immediately from pragmatics) to syntax. The situation is quite different if we wish to construct a language (or rather a language system, because we lay down rules), perhaps with the intention of practical application, as for making communications or formulating a scientific theory. Here we are not bound by a previous use of language, but are free to construct in accordance with our wishes and purposes. The construction of a language system Z may consist in laying down two kinds of rules, the semantical rules (Z-S or briefly S) and the syntactical rules (calculus Z-C or C). As a common basis for both, according to our former discussion, we have to make a classification of the signs which we intend to use and lay down rules of formation Z-F. Z-S consists of two parts, rules for the descriptive signs (Z-SD or SD) and rules for the logical signs (Z-SL or SL).

In constructing the system Z, we can proceed in two different ways—different as to the order of S and C. Here the order is not unessential, for, if we have chosen some rules arbitrarily, we are no longer free in the choice of others.

The first method consists in first constructing S and then constructing C. We start with a classification of the kinds of signs which we want, and rules F determining the forms of sentences which we intend to use. Then we lay down the rules SD; we choose objects, properties, etc., for which we wish to have direct designations, and then signs to designate these objects, properties, etc. Next we construct the rules SL; we choose signs to be used as logical signs and state for each of them the conditions of the truth of the sentences constructed with its help. (As mentioned before, we may also proceed by indicating the translations of the sentences containing logical signs, or giving their designata.) After this we proceed to syntax and construct the calculus C, e.g., by stating primitive sentences and rules of inference. It has been explained already that, if S is given or constructed, we are limited in constructing C in some essential respects, because C must be such that S is a true interpretation of C; but we are free in other respects.

The *second method* for constructing Z is first to construct C and then S. We begin again with a classification of signs and a system F of syntactical rules of formation, defining 'sentence in C' in a formal way. Then we set up the system C of syntactical rules of transformation, in other words, a formal definition of 'C-true' and 'C-implicate'. Since so far nothing has been determined concerning the single signs, we may choose these definitions, i.e., the rules of formation and of transformation, in any way we wish. With respect to a calculus to be constructed there is only a question of expedience or fitness to purposes chosen, but not of correctness. This will be discussed later.

Then we add to the uninterpreted calculus C an interpretation S. Its function is to determine truth conditions for the sentences of C and thereby to change them from formulas to propositions. We proceed in the following way. It is already determined by the rules F which expressions are formulas in C. Now we have to stipulate that each of them is also a proposition in S. By the syntactical classification of the signs it is not yet completely settled which signs are logical and which descriptive. In many cases there is still a considerable amount of freedom of choice in this respect, as we shall see later in some examples. After having stated which signs are to be logical and which descriptive, we construct the rules SL for the logical signs. Here our choice is restricted to some extent by the requirement that the interpretation must be true.

Finally we establish the rules SD for the descriptive signs. Here we have to take into account the classification of signs. We choose the designata for each kind of signs and then for each sign of that kind. We may begin with individual names. First we choose a field of objects with which we wish to deal in the language to be constructed, e.g., the persons of a certain group, the towns of a certain country, the colors, geometrical structures, or whatever else. Then we determine for each individual name, as its designatum, one object of the class chosen. Then, for each predicate, we choose a possible property of those objects, etc. In this way, a designatum for every descriptive sign is chosen. If we decide to make S an L-true interpretation of C, we have a great amount of freedom for the choice of the rules SD. Otherwise, we find some essential restrictions. If some of the C-true formulas are to become factual propositions, they must be factually true. Therefore, in this case, on the basis of our factual knowledge about the objects which we have chosen as subject matter of Z, we have to take care that the interpretations for the descriptive names, predicates, etc., i.e., their designata, are chosen in such a way that those factual C-true sentences are actually true.

12. Is Logic a Matter of Convention?

There has been much controversial discussion recently on the question whether or not logic is conventional. Are the rules on which logical deduction is based to be chosen at will and, hence, to be judged only with respect to convenience but not to correctness? Or is there a distinction between objectively right and objectively wrong systems so that in constructing a system of rules we are free only in relatively minor respects (as, e.g., the way of formulation) but bound in all essential respects? Obviously, the question discussed refers to the rules of an interpreted language, applicable for purposes of communication; nobody doubts that the rules of a pure calculus, without regard to any interpretation, can be chosen arbitrarily. On the basis of our former discussions we are in a position to answer the question. We found the possibility—which we called the second method— of constructing a language system in such a way that first a calculus C is established and then an interpretation is given by adding a semantical system S. Here we are free in choosing the rules of C. To be sure, the choice is not irrelevant; it depends upon C whether the interpretation can yield a rich language or only a poor one.

We may find that a calculus we have chosen yields a language which is too poor or which in some other respect seems unsuitable for the purpose we have in mind. But there is no question of a calculus being right or wrong, true or false. A true interpretation is possible for any given consistent calculus (and hence for any calculus of the usual kind, not containing rules for 'C-false'), however the rules may be chosen.

On the other hand, those who deny the conventional character of logic, i.e., the possibility of a free choice of the logical rules of deduction, are equally right in what they mean if not in what they say. They are right under a certain condition, which presumably is tacitly assumed. The condition is that the "meanings" of the logical signs are given before the rules of deduction are formulated. They would, for instance, insist that the rule R 1 of B-C ('from 'wenn . . . , so - - -' and '. . .', '- - -' is directly derivable' [§ 9]) is necessary; that it would be wrong to change it arbitrarily, e.g., into R 1*: 'from 'wenn . . . , so - - -' and 'nicht . . .', '- - -' is directly derivable'. What they presumably mean is that the rule R 1* is incorrect on the basis of the presupposed "meaning" of the signs 'wenn', 'so', and 'nicht'. Thus they have in mind the procedure which we called the first method (§ 11): we begin by establishing the semantical rules SL or assume them as given—obviously this is meant by saying that the "meaning" is given—and then we ask what rules of deduction, i.e., syntactical rules of transformation, would be in accordance with the presupposed semantical rules. In this order of procedure, we are, as we have seen, indeed bound in the choice of the rules in all essential respects. Thus we come to a reconciliation of the opposing views. And it seems to me that an agreement should easily be attainable in the other direction as well. The anti-conventionalists would certainly not deny that the rule R 1* can also be chosen and can lead to correct results, provided we interpret the logical signs in a different way (in the example given, we could interpret 'wenn . . . , so - - -', e.g., as '. . . or - - -').

The result of our discussion is the following: logic or the rules of deduction (in our terminology, the syntactical rules of transformation) can be chosen arbitrarily and hence are conventional if they are taken as the basis of the construction of the language system and if the interpretation of the system is later superimposed. On the other hand, a system of logic is not a matter of choice, but either right or wrong, if an interpretation of the logical signs is given in advance. But even here, conventions are of fundamental importance; for the basis on which logic is constructed, namely, the interpretation of the logical signs (e.g., by a determination of truth conditions) can be freely chosen.

It is important to be aware of the conventional components in the construction of a language system. This view leads to an unprejudiced investigation of the various forms of new logical systems which differ more or less from the customary form (e.g., the intuitionist logic constructed by Brouwer and Heyting, the systems of logic of modalities as constructed by Lewis and others, the systems of plurivalued logic as constructed by Lukasiewicz and Tarski, etc.), and it encourages the construction of further new forms. The task is not to decide which of the different systems is "the right logic" but to examine their formal properties and the possibilities for their interpretation and application in science. It might be that a system deviating from the ordinary form will turn out to be useful as a basis for the language of science.

III. Calculi and Their Application in Empirical Science

13. Elementary Logical Calculi

For any given calculus there are, in general, many different possibilities of a true interpretation. The practical situation, however, is such that for almost every calculus which is actually interpreted and applied in science, there is a certain interpretation or a certain kind of interpretation used in the great majority of cases of its practical application. This we will call the *customary interpretation* (or kind of interpretation) for the calculus. In what follows we shall discuss some calculi and their application. We classify them according to their customary interpretation in this way: logical calculi (in the narrower sense), mathematical, geometrical, and (other) physical calculi. The customary interpretation of the logical and mathematical calculi is a logical, L-determinate interpretation; that of the geometrical and physical calculi is descriptive and factual. The mathematical calculi are a special kind of logical calculi, distinguished merely by their greater complexity. The geometrical calculi are a special kind of physical calculi. This classification is rather rough and is only meant to serve a temporary, practical purpose.

To the logical calculi (in the narrower sense) belong most of the calculi of elementary structure used in symbolic logic, above all, the so-called sentential calculus and the so-called lower functional calculus. The *sentential calculus* has approximately the structure of B-C with F 4 and PS 4 omitted. The customary interpretation corresponds to the rules B-SL 2, 3. The form mostly used contains, however, only those signs which are logical in the customary interpretation, corresponding to the English words 'not', 'if', 'or', 'and', and the like, and sentential variables. The *lower functional calculus* (or predicate calculus) contains the sentential calculus and, in addition, general sentences with individual variables, namely, universal sentences (interpretation: 'for every x, ... ') and existential sentences (interpretation: 'there is an x such that ... '). Within symbolic logic, this calculus too is mostly used without descriptive signs but with three kinds of variables: sentential variables, individual variables (as in B-C), and predicate variables. The customary interpretation is a logical one, as given by B-SL. In the case of the logical calculi here explained the customary interpretation is the only one which is ever used practically. (If the calculi are supplemented in a certain way, it is even the only possible true interpretation.) Therefore, we shall call it the *normal interpretation* of the logical calculus.

If a calculus C is constructed with the intention of using it mostly or exclusively with a certain interpretation S, it may often seem convenient to use as signs of C not artificial symbols but those words of the word-language whose ordinary use is approximately in acccord with the interpretation intended (a word with exact accordance will usually not be available). Then we have in C the same sentences as in the interpreted language S, which is perhaps to be applied in science; "the same sentences" as to the wording, but in C they are formulas, while they are propositions in S. This procedure is mostly chosen in geometrical and other physical calculi (for examples see end of § 17, beginning of § 22).

In what follows we shall do the same for the logical calculus (where, for good reasons, it is usually not done). Thus, instead of symbols, we shall use the words 'not', 'if', etc. It has been shown (by H. M. Sheffer) that two primitive signs are sufficient, namely, 'excludes' (to be interpreted later) and 'for every'. It is not necessary to take as many primitive signs as we did in B-C, corresponding to 'not', 'if—then', 'for every'. The other logical signs of the logical calculus can be introduced by definitions. The primitive signs mentioned and all signs defined with their help are called logical constants. We shall use three kinds of variables: sentential variables ('p', 'q', etc.), individual variables ('x', 'y', etc., as in B-C), and predicate variables ('F',

'*G*', etc.). For a sentential variable a sentence may be substituted, for an individual variable an individual name, for a predicate variable a predicate, and for '*Fx*' an expression of sentential form containing the variable '*x*'.

A *definition* is a rule of a calculus which serves for introducing a new sign. In simpler cases the rule states that the new sign is to be taken as an abbreviation for a certain expression consisting only of old signs (i.e., primitive signs or signs defined earlier). In other cases the rule states that sentences containing the new sign and old signs are to be taken as abbreviations for certain sentences containing old signs only. Rules of the first kind are called explicit definitions (e.g., Defs. 11, 12, and 13 in § 14); those of the second kind are called definitions in use (e.g., Defs. 1–7, below); we shall use still another kind of definition, the so-called recursive definitions frequently found in arithmetic (e.g., Defs. 14 and 15 in § 14). The definitions in a calculus are, so to speak, additional rules of transformation, either primitive sentences or rules of inference, according to their formulation; they are added in order to provide shorter expressions. If a calculus C contains definitions and the interpretation S contains semantical rules for the primitive signs of C, the interpretation of the defined signs need not be given explicitly. The definitions, together with those rules of S, determine the truth conditions of the sentences containing the defined signs and thereby the interpretation of these signs.

We shall formulate the definitions here in this form: ' '. . .' for '- - -' '. This means that '. . .' is to serve as an abbreviation for '- - -', i.e., that '. . .' and '- - -', and likewise two expressions constructed out of '. . .' and '- - -' by the same substitutions, may always be replaced by each other. In this calculus, we take as simplest form of sentences in the beginning '*Fx*' (e.g., 'city Chicago' instead of 'Chicago is a city'); the usual form with 'is a' is introduced later by Definition 7.

The expressions included in parentheses serve merely to facilitate understanding; in the exact formulation they have to be omitted. The brackets and commas, however, are essential; they indicate the structure of the sentence (cf. § 5).

Def. 1. 'not p' for 'p excludes p'.

Def. 2. 'p or q' for 'not p, excludes, not q'.

Def. 3. 'p and q' for 'not [p excludes q]'.

Def. 4. 'if p then q' for 'not p, or q'.

Def. 5. 'p if and only if q' for '[if p then q] and [if q then p]'.

Def. 6. 'for some x, Fx' for 'not [for every x, not Fx]'.

Def. 7. 'x is an F' for 'Fx'.

The rules of transformation of the sentential calculus and the functional calculus will not be given here. They are not essentially different from those of B-C. It has been shown (by J. Nicod) that, if 'excludes' is taken as primitive sign, one primitive sentence is sufficient for the sentential calculus. For the lower functional calculus we have to add one more primitive sentence for 'for every', analogous to PS 4 in B-C.

The *normal interpretation* for the logical calculus is a logical one. Therefore, if interpreted, it is, so to speak, a skeleton of a language rather than a language proper, i.e., one capable of describing facts. It becomes a factual language only if supplemented by descriptive signs. These are then interpreted by SD-rules, and the logical constants by SL-rules. As SL-rules for the lower functional calculus we can state the following two rules for the two primitive signs. For the sentential calculus the first rule suffices.

1. A sentence of the form '. . . excludes - - -' is true if and only if not both '. . .' and '- - -' are true.

2. A sentence of the form 'for every . . . , - - -' is true if and only if all individuals have the property designated by '- - -' with respect to the variable '. . .'. (The individuals are the objects of the domain described, which is to be determined by an SD-rule.)

The interpretation of the defined signs 'not', etc., is determined by rule (1) and Definition 1, etc. The interpretation of 'not' and 'if—then' is easily seen to be the same as that of 'nicht', and 'wenn—so' in B-SL. (The truth conditions here given by rule [1] and Definitions 1–5 are the same as those which in symbolic logic usually are stated with the help of truth-value tables for the corresponding symbols, the so-called connectives.)

14. Higher Logical Calculi

The lower functional calculus can be enlarged to the higher functional calculus by the addition of predicates of higher levels. The predicates occurring in the lower functional calculus are now called predicates of first level; they designate properties of first level, i.e., properties of individuals. Now we introduce predicates of second level, which designate properties of second level, i.e., properties of properties of first level; predicates of third level designating properties of third level, etc. Further, new kinds of variables for these predicates of higher levels are introduced. (In the subsequent definitions we shall use as variables for predicates of second level '*m*' and '*n*', for predicates of third level '*K*'.) Expressions of the form 'for every . . .', and analogously 'for some . . .' (Def. 6), are now admitted not only for individual variables but also for predicate variables of any level. Some new rules of transformation for these new kinds of variables have to be added. We shall not give them here. Some of them are still controversial.

The *normal interpretation* of the higher functional calculus can again be given by two semantical rules. Rule (1) is kept, as the sentential calculus remains the basis for the higher functional calculus. Rule (2) must be replaced by the subsequent rule (2*), because of the extended use of 'for every'. For individual variables, (2*) is in accordance with (2). (It may be remarked that there are some controversies and unsolved problems concerning the properties of higher levels.)

2*. A sentence of the form 'for every . . . , - - -' is true if and only if all entities belonging to the range of the variable '. . .' have the property designated by '- - -' with respect to '. . .'. (To the range of an individual variable belong all individuals, to the range of a predicate variable of level *r* belong all properties of level *r*.)

To the definitions which we stated in the lower functional calculus, new ones can now be added which make use of predicates and variables of higher levels. We shall first give some

rough explanations of the new expressions and later the definitions. First, identity can be defined; '$x = y$' is to say that x is the
same object as y; this is defined by 'x and y have all properties in
common' (Def. 8). Then we shall define the concept of a cardinal number of a property, restricting ourselves, for the sake
of simplicity, to finite cardinal numbers. 'F is an m' is to say
that the property F has the cardinal number m; i.e., that there
are m objects with the property F. This concept is defined by a
recursive definition (for finite cardinals only). 'F is a 0' is defined as saying that no object has the property F (Def. 9a).
Then 'F is an m^+', where 'm^+' designates the next cardinal number greater than m, i.e., $m+1$, is defined in the following way
in terms of 'm': there is a property G with the cardinal number
m such that all objects which have the property G, and, in addition, some object x, but no other objects, have the property F
(Def. 9b). A property K of numbers is called hereditary if,
whenever a number m is a K, $m+1$ is also a K. Then 'm is a
finite cardinal number' can be defined (as Frege has shown) in
this way: m has all hereditary properties of 0 (Def. 10). The
numerals '1', '2', etc., can easily be defined by '0^+', '1^+', etc.
(Def. 11, etc.). The sum ('$m+n$') and the product ('$m \times n$') can
be defined by recursive definitions, as is customary in arithmetic (Defs. 14 and 15).

Def. 8. '$x = y$' for 'for every (property) F, if x is an F then y is an F'.
Analogously for any higher level.

Def. 9a. 'F is a 0' for 'not [for some x, x is an F]'.
  b. 'F is an m^+' for 'for some G, for some x, for every y [[y is an F if
and only if [y is a G or $y = x$]] and G is an m and, not x is a G].

Def. 10. 'm is a finite cardinal number' for 'for every (property of numbers)
K, if [0 is a K and, for every n [if n is a K then n^+ is a K]] then m
is a K'.

Def. 11. '1' for '0^+'.
Def. 12. '2' for '1^+'.
Def. 13. '3' for '2^+'.
Analogously for any further numeral.

Def. 14a. '$m+0$' for 'm'.
  b. '$m+n^+$' for '[$m+n]^+$'.
Def. 15a. '$m \times 0$' for '0'.
  b. '$m \times n^+$' for '[$m \times n] + m$'.

For the reasons mentioned before we have used, instead of arbitrary symbols, words whose ordinary use agrees approximately with the interpretation intended. It is, however, to be noticed that their exact interpretation in our language system is not to be derived from their ordinary use but from their definition in connection with the semantical rules (1) and (2*).

We see that it is possible to define within the logical calculus signs for numbers and arithmetical operations. It can further be shown that all theorems of ordinary arithmetic are provable in this calculus, if suitable rules of transformation are established.

The method of constructing a calculus of arithmetic within a logical calculus was first found by Frege (1884) and was then developed by Russell (1903) and Whitehead (1910). (Defs. 9–15 are, in their essential features, in accordance with Frege and Russell, but make use of some simplifications due to the recent development of symbolic logic.) We shall later outline another form of an arithmetical calculus (§ 17) and discuss the problem of mathematics more in detail (§ 20).

15. Application of Logical Calculi

The chief function of a logical calculus in its application to science is not to furnish logical theorems, i.e., L-true sentences, but to guide the deduction of factual conclusions from factual premises. (In most presentations of logical systems the first point, the proofs, is overemphasized; the second, the derivations, neglected.)

For the following discussions we may make a rough distinction between *singular* and *universal* sentences among factual sentences. By a singular sentence of the language of science or of an interpreted calculus we mean a sentence concerning one or several things (or events or space-time-points), describing, e.g., a property of a thing or a relation between several things. By a universal sentence we mean a sentence concerning all objects of the field in question, e.g., all things or all space-time-points. A report about a certain event or a description of a certain landscape consists of singular sentences; on the other hand, the so-called laws of nature in any field (physics, biology, psychology, etc.) are universal. The simplest kind of an application of the logical calculus to factual sentences is the derivation of a singular sentence from other singular sentences (see, e.g., the second example of a derivation in B-C, end of § 9). Of greater practical importance is the deduction of a singular sentence from premises which include both singular and universal sentences. We are involved in this kind of a deduction if we explain a known fact or if we predict an unknown fact. The form of the deduction is the same for these two cases. We have had this form in the first example of a derivation in B-C (§ 9); we find it again in the following example, which contains, besides signs of the logical calculus, some descriptive signs. In an application of the logical calculus, some descriptive signs have to be introduced as primitive; others may then be defined on their basis. SD-rules must then be laid down in order to establish the interpretation intended by the scientist. Premiss (3) is the law of thermic expansion in qualitative formulation. In later examples we shall apply the same law in quantitative formulation (D_1 in § 19; D_2 in § 23).

Premises:
1. c is an iron rod.
2. c is now heated.
3. for every x, if x is an iron rod and x is heated, x expands.

Conclusion: 4. c now expands.

A deduction of this form can occur in two practically quite different kinds of situations. In the first case we may have found (4) by observation and ask the physicist to explain the fact observed. He gives the *explanation* by referring to other facts (1) and (2) and a law (3). In the second case we may have found by observation the facts (1) and (2) but not (4). Here the deduction with the help of the law (3) supplies the prediction (4), which may then be tested by further observations.

The example given shows only a very short deduction, still more abbreviated by the omission of the intermediate steps between premises and conclusion. But a less trivial deduction consisting of many steps of inference has fundamentally the same nature. In practice a deduction in science is usually made by a few jumps instead of many steps. It would, of course, be practically impossible to give each deduction which occurs the form of a complete derivation in the logical calculus, i.e., to dissolve it into single steps of such a kind that each step is the application of one of the rules of transformation of the calculus, including the definitions. An ordinary reasoning of a few seconds would then take days. But it is essential that this dissolution is theoretically possible and practically possible for any small part of the process. Any critical point can thus be put under the logical microscope and enlarged to the degree desired. In consequence of this, a scientific controversy can be split up into two fundamentally different components, a factual and a logical (including here the mathematical). With respect to the logical component the opponents can come to an agreement only by first agreeing upon the rules of the logical calculus to be applied and the L-semantical rules for its interpretation, and by then applying these rules, disregarding the interpretation of the descriptive signs. The discussion, of course, need not concern the whole calculus; it will be sufficient to expand the critical part of the controversial deduction to the degree required by the situation. The critical point will usually not be within the elementary part of the logical calculus (to which all examples of derivations discussed above belong), but to a more complex calculus, e.g., the higher, mathematical part of the logical calculus, or a specific mathematical calculus, or a physical calculus. This will be discussed later; then the advantage of the formal procedure will become more manifest.

16. General Remarks about Nonlogical Calculi (Axiom Systems)

In later sections we shall discuss certain other calculi which are applied in science. The logical calculus explained previously is distinguished from them by the fact that it serves as their basis. Each of the nonlogical calculi to be explained later consists, strictly speaking, of two parts: a logical *basic calculus* and a *specific calculus* added to it. The basic calculus could be approximately the same for all those calculi; it could consist of the sentential calculus and a smaller or greater part of the functional calculus as previously outlined. The specific partial calculus does not usually contain additional rules of inference but only additional primitive sentences, called *axioms*. As the basic calculus is essentially the same for all the different specific calculi, it is customary not to mention it at all but to describe only the specific part of the calculus. What usually is called an *axiom system* is thus the second part of a calculus whose character as a part is usually not noticed. For any of the mathematical and physical axiom systems in their ordinary form it is necessary to add a logical basic calculus. Without its help it would not be possible to prove any theorem of the system or to carry out any deduction by use of the system. Not only is a basic logical calculus tacitly presupposed in the customary formulation of an axiom system but so also is a special interpretation of the logical calculus, namely, that which we called the normal interpretation. An axiom system contains, besides the logical constants, other constants which we may call its specific or axiomatic constants. Some of them are taken as primitive; others may be defined. The definitions lead back to the primitive specific signs and logical signs. An interpretation of an axiom system is given by semantical rules for some of the specific signs, since for the logical signs the normal interpretation is presupposed. If semantical rules for the primitive specific signs are given, the interpretation of the defined specific signs is indirectly determined by these rules together with the definitions. But it is also possible—and sometimes convenient, as we shall see—to give the interpretation by laying down semantical rules for another suitable selection of specific signs, not including the primitive signs. If all specific signs are interpreted as logical signs, the interpretation is a logical and L-determinate one; otherwise it is a descriptive one. (Every logical interpretation is L-determinate; the converse does not always hold.)

17. An Elementary Mathematical Calculus

We take here as mathematical calculi those whose customary interpretation is mathematical, i.e., in terms of numbers and functions of numbers. As an example, we shall give the classical axiom system of Peano for (elementary) arithmetic. It is usually called an axiom system of arithmetic because in its customary interpretation it is interpreted as a theory of natural numbers, as we shall see. This interpretation is, however, by no means the only important one. The logical basic calculus presupposed has to include the lower functional calculus and some part of the higher, up to expressions 'for every F' for predicate variables of first level and Definition 8 for '$=$' (§ 14). The specific primitive signs are 'b', 'N', '''. (The following axioms, of course, are, within the calculus, independent of any interpretation. Nevertheless, the reader who is not familiar with them will find it easier to conceive their form and function by looking at their interpretation given below.)

Axiom System of Peano:

P 1. b is an N.

P 2. For every x, if x is an N, then x' is an N.

P 3. For every x, y, if [x is an N and y is an N and $x'=y'$] then $x=y$.

P 4. For every x, if x is an N, then, not $b=x'$.

P 5. For every F, if [b is an F and, for every x [if x is an F then x' is an F]] then [for every y, if y is an N then y is an F].

　　(Briefly: if F is any property of b which is hereditary [from x to x'] then all N are F.)

It is easy to see that any number of true *interpretations* of this calculus can be constructed. We have only to choose any infinite class, to select one of its elements as the beginning member of a sequence and to state a rule determining for any given member of the sequence its immediate successor. (An order of elements of this kind is called a progression.) Then we interpret in this way: 'b' designates the beginning member of the sequence; if '. . .' designates a member of the sequence then '. . .$'$' designates its immediate successor; 'N' designates the class of all members of the sequence that can be reached from the beginning member in a finite number of steps. It can easily be shown that in any interpretation of this kind the five axioms become true.

Example: 'b' designates August 14, 1938; if '. . .' designates a day, '. . .$'$' designates the following day; 'N' designates the class (supposed to be infinite) of all days from August 14, 1938, on. This interpretation of the Peano system is descriptive, while the customary one is logical.

The *customary interpretation* of the Peano system may first be formulated in this way: 'b' designates the cardinal number 0; if '. . .' designates a cardinal number n, then '. . .'' designates the next one, i.e., $n+1$; 'N' designates the class of finite cardinal numbers. Hence in this interpretation the system concerns the progression of finite cardinal numbers, ordered according to magnitude. Against the given semantical rule ' 'b' designates the cardinal number 0' perhaps the objection will be raised that the cardinal number 0 is not an object to which we could point, as to my desk. This remark is right; but it does not follow that the rule is incorrect. We shall give the interpretation in another way, with the help of a translation.

In the investigation of calculi the procedure of *translation* of one calculus into another is of great importance. A system of rules of translation of the calculus K_2 into the calculus K_1 determines for each primitive sign of K_2 an expression of K_1 called its correlated expression, and for each kind of variable in K_2 its correlated kind of variable in K_1. The rules must be such that the result of translating any sentence in K_2 is always a sentence in K_1. The translation is called C-true if the following three conditions are fulfilled: (1) every C-true sentence in K_2 becomes, if translated, C-true in K_1; (2) every C-false sentence in K_2 becomes C-false in K_1; (3) if the relation of C-implication in K_2 holds among some sentences, then the relation of C-implication in K_1 holds among those into which they are translated. If we have an interpretation I_1 for the calculus K_1, then the translation of K_2 into K_1 determines in connection with I_1 an interpretation I_2 for K_2. I_2 may be called a *secondary interpretation*. If the translation is C-true and the (primary) interpretation I_1 is true, I_2 is also true.

We shall now state rules of translation for the Peano system into the higher functional calculus and thereby give a secondary interpretation for that system. The logical basic calculus is translated into itself; thus we have to state the correlation only for the specific primitive signs. As correlates for 'b', '''', 'N', we take '0', '+', 'finite cardinal number'; for any variable a variable two levels higher. Accordingly, the five axioms are translated into the following sentences of the logical calculus.

P′ 1. 0 is a finite cardinal number.

P′ 2. For every m, if m is a finite cardinal number, then m^+ is a finite cardinal number.

P′ 3. For every m, n, if [m is a finite cardinal number and n is a finite cardinal number and $m^+ = n^+$] then $m = n$.

P′ 4. For every m, if m is a finite cardinal number, then, not $0 = m^+$.

P′ 5. For every K, if [0 is a K and, for every m [if m is a K then m^+ is a K]] then [for every n, if n is a finite cardinal number then n is a K].

The *customary interpretation* of the Peano system can now be formulated in another way. This interpretation consists of the given translation together with the normal interpretation of the higher functional calculus up to the third level. (P′ 5 contains a variable of this level.)

The whole interpretation is thus built up in the following way. We have two L-semantical rules for the primitive signs 'excludes' and 'for every' of the logical calculus, indicating truth conditions (rules [1] and [2*] in § 14). Then we have a chain of definitions leading to Definitions 9a and b and 11 for '0', '+', and 'finite cardinal number' (§ 14). Finally we have rules of translation which correlate these defined signs of the logical calculus to the primitive signs 'b', '′', and 'N' of the Peano system.

If we assume that the normal interpretation of the logical calculus is true, the given secondary interpretation for the Peano system is shown to be true by showing that the correlates of the axioms are C-true. And it can indeed be shown that the sentences P′ 1–5 are provable in the higher functional calculus, provided suitable rules of transformation are established. As the normal interpretation of the logical calculus is logical and L-true, the given interpretation of the Peano system is also logical and L-true.

We can now define signs within the Peano axiom system which correspond to the signs '0', '1', etc., '+', etc., of the logical calculus. For greater clarity we distinguish them by the subscript 'P'. (In an arithmetical calculus, however—whether in the form of Peano's or some other—one ordinarily does not use arbitrary symbols like '*b*' or '0_P', '*b'*' or '1_P', '$+_P$', etc., but, because of the customary interpretation, the corresponding signs of the ordinary language '0', '1', '+', etc.)

Def. P 1. '0_P' for '*b*'.
Def. P 2. '1_P' for '*b'*'.
Def. P 3. '2_P' for '*b''*'.
  Etc.
Def. P 4a. '$x +_P 0_P$' for '*x*'.
      b. '$x +_P y'$' for '$[x +_P y]'$'.
Def. P 5a. '$x \times_P 0_P$' for '0_P'.
      b. '$x \times_P y'$' for '$[x \times_P y] +_P x$'.

Thus the natural numbers and functions of them can be defined both in the logical calculus and in a specific arithmetical calculus, e.g., that of Peano. And the theorems of ordinary arithmetic are provable in both calculi. (Strictly speaking, they are not the same theorems in the different calculi, but corresponding theorems; if, however, the same signs are used—and, as mentioned before, this is convenient and usual—then corresponding theorems consist even of the same signs.)

18. Higher Mathematical Calculi

On the basis of a calculus of the arithmetic of natural numbers the whole edifice of classical mathematics can be erected without the use of new primitive signs. Whether a specific calculus of arithmetic or the logical calculus is taken as a basis does not make an essential difference, once the translation of the first into the second is established. It is not possible to outline here the construction of mathematics; we can make only a few remarks. There are many different possibilities for the introduction of further kinds of numbers. A simple method is the following one. The integers (positive and negative) are defined as pairs of natural numbers, the fractions as pairs of integers, the real numbers as classes either of integers or of fractions, the complex numbers as pairs of real numbers. Another way of introducing any one of these kinds of numbers consists in constructing a new specific calculus in which the numbers of that kind are taken as individuals, like the natural numbers in the Peano calculus.

This has been done especially for the real numbers. A specific calculus of this kind can be translated in one way or another into a more elementary specific calculus or into the logical calculus. (Example: The individual expressions of a specific calculus of real numbers may be translated into expressions for classes of integers or of fractions either in the Peano calculus or in the logical calculus.) For each of the kinds of numbers, functions (summation, multiplication, etc.) can be defined. Further, the concept of limit can be defined, and with its help the fundamental concepts of the infinitesimal calculus, the differential coefficient, and the integral.

If a mathematical calculus is based on the Peano calculus by the use of definitions, then its customary interpretation is determined by that of the latter. If, on the other hand, a mathematical calculus is constructed as an independent specific calculus, we can give an interpretation for it by translating it either into an enlarged Peano system or into an enlarged logical calculus (as indicated above for a calculus of real numbers.) Here we can scarcely speak of "the" customary interpretation, but only of the set of customary interpretations. Their forms may differ widely from one another; but they have in common the character of logical interpretations. If the interpretation is given by a translation either into the Peano system with reference to its customary interpretation or by a translation into the logical calculus with reference to its normal interpretation, this character is obvious. In a customary interpretation of a mathematical calculus every sign in it is interpreted as a logical sign, and hence every sentence consists only of logical signs and is therefore L-determinate (see § 7).

If we choose the form of the construction of mathematics within the logical calculus, we do not even need a translation; the interpretation is simply the normal interpretation of the logical calculus. In this case every mathematical sign is defined on the basis of the two primitive signs of the logical calculus, and hence every mathematical sentence is an abbreviation for a sentence containing, besides variables, only those two signs. In most cases, though, this sentence would be so long that it would not be possible to write it down within a lifetime. Therefore, the abbreviations introduced in the construction of mathematics are not only convenient but practically indispensable.

19. Application of Mathematical Calculi

The application of mathematical calculi in empirical science is not essentially different from that of logical calculi. Since mathematical sentences are, in the customary interpretation, L-determinate, they cannot have factual content; they do not convey information about facts which would have to be taken into consideration besides those described in empirical science. The function of mathematics for empirical science consists in providing, first, forms of expression shorter and more efficient than non-mathematical linguistic forms and, second, modes of logical deduction shorter and more efficient than those of elementary logic.

Mathematical calculi with their customary interpretation are distinguished from elementary logical calculi chiefly by the occurrence of numerical expressions. There are two procedures in empirical science which lead to the application of numerical expressions: counting and measurement (cf. Lenzen, Vol. I, No. 5, §§ 4 and 5). Counting is ascertaining the cardinal number of a class of single, separate things or of events. Measuring is ascertaining the value of a magnitude for a certain thing or place at a certain time. For each physical magnitude, e.g., length, weight, temperature, electric field, etc., there are one or several methods of measurement. The result of a measurement is a fraction or a real number. (Irrational real numbers can also occur, but only if, besides direct measurement, calculation is applied.) If a deduction has to do with results of counting, we may apply, besides an elementary logical calculus, a calculus of elementary arithmetic. If it has to do with results of measurements, we may apply a calculus of analysis, i.e., of real numbers.

Let us look at a very simple example of a logico-mathematical deduction. We apply a certain part of the higher functional calculus and an arithmetical calculus. We presuppose for the following derivation that in this arithmetical calculus the sentence

'3+6 = 9' (7) has been proved earlier. Whether we take the arithmetical calculus in the form of a part of the higher functional calculus (as in § 14) or in the form of a specific calculus (as in § 17) does not make any essential difference; in both cases sentence (7) is provable. In order to keep in closer contact with ordinary language, we use the following definition: 'there are m F's' for 'F is an m'; further, we write 'n.i.t.r.' for 'now in this room'.

Premisses

1. There are 3 students n.i.t.r.
2. There are 6 girls n.i.t.r.
3. For every x [x is a person n.i.t.r. if and only if [x is a student n.i.t.r. or x is a girl n.i.t.r.]].
4. For every x [if x is a girl n.i.t.r., then, not x is a student n.i.t.r.].

Defs. 1–9, 14

5. For every F, G, H, m, n [if [m and n are finite cardinal numbers and G is an m and H is an n and for every x [x is an F if and only if, x is a G or x is an H] and for every y [if y is a G then, not y is an H]] then F is an $m+n$].

[This says that, if a class F is divided into two parts, G and H, the cardinal number of F is the sum of the cardinal numbers of G and H.]

(1)(2)(3)(4)(5)

6. There are 3+6 persons n.i.t.r.

Arithmet. theorem:

7. 3+6 = 9.

(6)(7) *Conclusion:*

8. There are 9 persons n.i.t.r.

The premisses of this derivation describe some facts empirically established by observation (including counting). The conclusion is also a factual sentence; but its content, the amount of factual information it conveys, does not go beyond that of the premisses. We have discussed earlier (at the end of § 9) the application of proved theorems in a derivation; here (5) and (7) are examples of this method. These sentences do not contribute to the factual content of the conclusion; they merely help in transforming the premisses into the conclusion. To say that the result (8) is "calculated" from the data (1)–(4), means just this: it is obtained by a formal procedure involving a mathematical calculus. The effect of the application of a mathematical calculus is always, as in this example, the possibility of presenting in a shorter and more easily apprehensible way facts already known.

Here an objection will perhaps be raised. That the application of mathematics consists merely in a transformation of the premisses without adding anything to what they say about the facts, may be true in trivial cases like the example given. If, however, we predict, with the help of mathematics, a future event, do we not come to a new factual content? Let us discuss an example of a derivation of this kind. The derivation—called D_1—leads to the prediction of a thermic expansion as in a former example (§ 15), but now with quantitative determinations. The premisses of D_1 relate the results of measurements of the temperature of an iron rod at two time-points and its length at the first; further, the law of thermic expansion is one of the premisses, but now in quantitative formulation; and, finally, there is included a statement of the coefficient of thermic expansion. The conclusion states the amount of the expansion of the rod. We shall not represent D_1 here in detail because a similar derivation D_2 will be discussed later (§ 23); the premisses of D_1 are not only the sentences (1)–(5) of D_2 but also (6) and (10); the conclusion in D_1 is the same as in D_2. In D_1 a calculus of real numbers (or at least of fractions) is applied. The conclusion describes a fact which has not yet been observed but could be tested by observations. Now, the question is whether the derivation D_1 does not lead, with the help of a mathematical calculus, to a factual content beyond that of the premisses. This might seem so if we look only at the singular sentences among the premisses. But two laws also belong to the premisses of D_1 (the sentences [6] and [10] of D_2). They are universal; they say that certain regularities hold not only in the cases so far observed but at any place at any time. Thus, these sentences are very comprehensive. The conclusion merely restates what is already stated by the universal premisses for all cases and hence also for the present case, but now explicitly for this case. Thus, the logico-mathematical derivation merely evolves what is implicitly involved in the premisses. To be sure, if we state a new law on the basis of certain observations, the law says much more than the observation sentences known; but this is not a deduction. If, on the other hand, a law is used within a derivation with the help of a logico-mathematical calculus, then the law must be among the premisses, and hence the conclusion does not say more than the premisses. The situation is different in the application of a physical calculus, as we shall see later (§ 23).

On the basis of the presupposed interpretation, the premisses and the conclusion of the derivation D_1 are factual. But D_1 also contains sentences which are proved in a logico-mathematical calculus and hence, when interpreted, are L-true, e.g., the sentences which in D_2 occur as (7) and (13) (§ 23). As explained before, derivations are immensely simplified by the method of laying down for any future use certain partial sequences occurring in many derivations and containing only provable sentences. Each sequence of this kind is a proof of its last sentence; wherever it occurs in other proofs or derivations it may be represented by its last element, i.e., the theorem proved. Thus a logical or mathematical theorem is, regarded from the point of view of its application in empirical science, a device or tool enabling us to make a very complex and long chain of applications of the rules of the calculus by one stroke, so to speak. The theorem is itself, even when interpreted, not a factual statement but an instrument facilitating operations with factual statements, namely, the deduction of a factual conclusion from factual premisses. The service which mathematics renders to empirical science consists in furnishing these instruments; the mathematician not only produces them for any particular case of application but keeps them in store, so to speak, ready for any need that may arise.

It is important to notice the distinction between 'primitive sentence' and 'premiss'. A primitive sentence of a calculus C (no matter whether it belongs to the basic calculus or is one of the specific axioms, and no matter whether, in an interpretation, it becomes L-true or factual) is stated as C-true by the rules of the calculus C. Therefore, it has to become a true proposition in any adequate (i.e., true) interpretation of C. The premisses of a derivation D in C, on the other hand, need not be C-true in C or true in a true interpretation of C. It is merely shown by D that a certain other sentence (the conclusion of D) is derivable from the premisses of D and must therefore, in a true interpretation, be true *if* the premisses happen to be true; but whether this is the case is not determined by D.

20. The Controversies over "Foundations" of Mathematics

There have been many discussions in modern times about the nature of mathematics in general and of the various kinds of numbers, and, further, about the distinction and relationship between knowledge in mathematics and knowledge in empirical science. In the course of the last century, mathematicians found that all mathematical signs can be defined on the basis of the signs of the theory of natural numbers.

The fundamental concepts of the infinitesimal calculus (differential coefficient and integral) were defined by Cauchy and Weierstrass in terms of the calculus of real numbers, with the help of the concept 'limit (of a sequence of real numbers)'. Thereby they succeeded in entirely eliminating the dubious concept of "infinitely small magnitudes" and thus giving the infinitesimal calculus a rigorous basis in the theory of real numbers. The next step was made by Frege and Russell, who defined real numbers as classes of natural numbers or of fractions. (Fractions can easily be defined as pairs of natural numbers.)

The reduction mentioned was entirely inside of mathematics. Therefore, it left the more general and fundamental problems unanswered. These have been discussed especially during the last fifty years, usually under the heading "foundations of mathematics". Among the different doctrines developed in this field, three are outstanding and most often discussed; they are known as logicism, formalism, and intuitionism. We will indicate briefly some characteristic features of the three movements. *Logicism* was founded by Frege and developed by Russell and Whitehead. Its chief thesis is that mathematics is a branch of logic. This thesis was demonstrated by constructing a system for the whole of classical mathematics within a logical calculus (see § 14 and some remarks in § 18). Truth conditions for the primitive signs of the logical calculus were given; thereby an interpretation for the whole mathematical system was determined. In this interpretation all mathematical signs became logical signs, all mathematical theorems L-true propositions.

Formalism, founded by Hilbert and Bernays, proposed, in contradistinction to logicism, to construct the system of classical mathematics as a mere calculus without regard to interpretation. The theory developed is called metamathematics; it is, in our terminology, a syntax of the language system of mathematics, involving no semantics. Hilbert's system is a combination of a logical basic calculus with a specific mathematical calculus using as specific primitive signs '0' and '′' as did Peano's system (§ 17). The controversy between the two doctrines concerning the question whether first to construct logic and then mathematics within logic without new primitive signs, or both simultaneously, has at present lost much of its former appearance of importance. We see today that the logico-mathematical calculus can be constructed in either way and that it does not make much difference which one we choose. If the method of logicism is chosen, constructing the system of mathematics as a part of the logical calculus, then by the normal interpretation of the latter we get an interpretation, and moreover the customary one, of the former. The formalists have not concerned themselves much with the question how the mathematical calculus, if constructed according to their method, is to be interpreted and applied in empirical science. As already explained (§ 17), the interpretation can be given by rules of translation for the specific primitive signs into the logical calculus. Another way would be to lay down L-semantical rules for these signs, stating the truth conditions for the descriptive sentences in which they occur. Formalists do not give an interpretation for the mathematical calculus and even seem to regard it as impossible for the nonelementary parts of the calculus, but they emphasize very much the need for a proof of the consistency for the mathematical calculus and even regard it as the chief task of metamathematics. There is some relation between the two questions; if a proof of consistency for a calculus can be given, then a true interpretation and application of the calculus is logically possible. So far, a proof of consistency has been given only for a certain part of arithmetic; the most comprehensive one has been constructed by Gentzen (1936).

Foundations of Logic and Mathematics

Gödel has shown (1931) that it is not possible to construct a proof for the consistency of a calculus C containing arithmetic, within a metalanguage possessing no other logical means (forms of expression and modes of deduction) than C. Hilbert's aim was to construct the proof of consistency in a "finitist" metalanguage (similar to an intuitionist system, see below). At the present, it is not yet known whether this aim can be reached in spite of Gödel's result. In any case, the concept of "finitist logic" is in need of further clarification.

The doctrine of *intuitionism* was originated by Brouwer (1912) and Weyl (1918) on the basis of earlier ideas of Kronecker and Poincaré. This doctrine rejects both the purely formal construction of mathematics as a calculus and the interpretation of mathematics as consisting of L-true sentences without factual content. Mathematics is rather regarded as a field of mental activities based upon "pure intuition". A definition, a sentence, or a deduction is only admitted if it is formulated in "constructive" terms; that is to say, a reference to a mere possibility is not allowed unless we know a method of actualizing it. Thus, for instance, the concept of provability (in the mathematical system) is rejected because there is no method which would lead, for any given sentence S, either to a proof for S or to a proof for the negation of S. It is only allowed to call a sentence proved after a proof has been constructed. For similar reasons, the principle of the excluded middle, the indirect proof of purely existential sentences, and other methods are rejected. In consequence, both elementary logic and classical mathematics are considerably curtailed and complicated. However, the boundary between the admissible and the nonadmissible is not stated clearly and varies with the different authors.

Concerning mathematics as a pure calculus there are no sharp controversies. These arise as soon as mathematics is dealt with as a system of "knowledge"; in our terminology, as an interpreted system. Now, if we regard interpreted mathematics as an instrument of deduction within the field of empirical knowledge rather than as a system of information, then many of the controversial problems are recognized as being questions not of truth but of technical expedience. The question is: Which form of the mathematical system is technically most suitable for the purpose mentioned? Which one provides the greatest safety?

If we compare, e.g., the systems of classical mathematics and of intuitionistic mathematics, we find that the first is much simpler and technically more efficient, while the second is more safe from surprising occurrences, e.g., contradictions. At the present time, any estimation of the degree of safety of the system of classical mathematics, in other words, the degree of plausibility of its principles, is rather subjective. The majority of mathematicians seem to regard this degree as sufficiently high for all practical purposes and therefore prefer the application of classical mathematics to that of intuitionistic mathematics. The latter has not, so far as I know, been seriously applied in physics by anybody.

The problems mentioned cannot here be discussed more in detail. Such discussion is planned for a later volume of this *Encyclopedia*. A more detailed discussion can be found in those of the books which deal with mathematics mentioned in the "Selected Bibliography" at the end of this monograph.

21. Geometrical Calculi and Their Interpretations

When we referred to mathematics in the previous sections, we did not mean to include geometry but only the mathematics of numbers and numerical functions. Geometry must be dealt with separately. To be sure, the geometrical calculi, aside from interpretation, are not fundamentally different in their character from the other calculi and, moreover, are closely related to the mathematical calculi. That is the reason why they too have been developed by mathematicians. But the customary interpretations of geometrical calculi are descriptive, while those of the mathematical calculi are logical.

A geometrical calculus is usually constructed as an axiom system, i.e., a specific calculus presupposing a logical calculus (with normal interpretation). Such a calculus describes a structure whose elements are left undetermined as long as we do not make an interpretation. The geometrical calculi describe many different structures. And for each structure, e.g., the Euclidean, there are many different possible forms of calculi describing it. As an example let us consider an axiom system of Euclidean geometry. We choose a form having six primitive signs; three for classes of individuals, 'P_1', 'P_2', 'P_3', and three for relations, 'I', 'B', 'K'. We write '$I(x,y)$' for 'the relation I holds between x and y', and '$B(x,y,z)$' for 'the (triadic) relation B holds for x,y,z'. We will give only a few examples out of the long series of axioms:

G 1. For every x, y [if [x is a P_1 and y is a P_1] then, for some z [z is a P_2 and $I(x,z)$ and $I(y,z)$]].

G 2. For every x [if x is a P_3 then, for some y [y is a P_1 and, not $I(y,x)$]].

G 3. For every x, y, z [if $B(x,y,z)$ then, not $B(y,x,z)$].

G 4. For every x, y, z [if [x is a P_1 and y is a P_2 and z is a P_3 and $I(x,z)$ and $I(y,z)$ and, not $I(x,y)$] then there is (exactly) 1 u such that [u is a P_2 and $I(x,u)$ and I (u,z) and, for every t [if $I(t,u)$ then, not $I(t,y)$]]]. (Euclidean parallel axiom.)

For a geometrical calculus there are many interpretations, and even many quite different and interesting interpretations, some of them logical, some descriptive. The *customary interpretation* is descriptive. It consists of a translation into the physical calculus (to be dealt with in the next section) together with the customary interpretation of the physical calculus. Rules of translation: (1) 'P_1' is translated into 'point', (2) 'P_2' into 'straight line', (3) 'P_3' into 'plane', (4) '$I(x,y)$' into 'x is lying on y' (incidence), (5) '$B(x,y,z)$' into 'the point x is between the points y and z on a straight line', (6) '$K(x,y,u,v)$' into 'the segment x,y is congruent with the segment u,v (i.e., the distance between x and y is equal to the distance between u and v)'. It is to be noticed that the words 'point', etc., are here signs of the physical calculus in its customary interpretation. Hence we may think of a point as a place in the space of nature; straight lines may be characterized by reference to light rays in a vacuum or to stretched threads; congruence may be characterized by referring to a method of measuring length, etc. Thus the specific signs of a geometrical calculus are interpreted as descriptive signs. (On the other hand, the specific signs of a mathematical calculus are interpreted as logical signs, even if they occur in descriptive factual sentences stating the results of counting or measuring; see, e.g., the logical sign '3', defined by Def. 13, § 14, occurring in premiss [1], § 19.) The axioms and theorems of a geometrical calculus are translated into descriptive, factual propositions of interpreted physics; they form a theory which we may call *physical geometry*, because it is a branch of physics, in contradistinction to mathematical geometry i.e., the geometrical calculus. As an example, the four axioms stated above are translated into the following sentences of the physical calculus (formulated here, for simplicity, in the forms of ordinary language).

PG 1. For any two points there is a straight line on which they lie.

PG 2. For any plane there is a point not lying on it.

PG 3. If the points x, y, and z lie on a straight line and x is between y and z, then y is not between x and z.

PG 4. If the point x and the line y lie in the plane z, but x not on y, then there is one and only one line u in the plane z such that x lies on u and no point is both on u and y (hence u is the parallel to y through x).

22. The Distinction between Mathematical and Physical Geometry

The distinction between mathematical geometry, i.e., the calculus, and physical geometry is often overlooked because both are usually called geometry and both usually employ the same terminology. Instead of artificial symbols like 'P_1', etc., the words 'point', 'line', etc., are used in mathematical geometry as well. The axioms are then not formulated like G 1–4 but like PG 1–4, and hence there is no longer any difference in formulation between mathematical and physical geometry. This procedure is very convenient in practice—like the analogous procedure in the mathematical calculus, mentioned previously—because it saves the trouble of translating, and facilitates the understanding and manipulating of the calculus. But it is essential to keep in mind the fundamental difference between mathematical and physical geometry in spite of the identity of formulation. The difference becomes clear when we take into consideration other interpretations of the geometrical calculus.

Of especial importance for the development of geometry in the past few centuries has been a certain translation of the geometrical calculus into the mathematical calculus. This leads, in combination with the customary interpretation of the mathematical calculus, to a logical interpretation of the geometrical calculus. The translation was found by Descartes and is known as analytic geometry or geometry of coordinates. 'P_1' (or, in ordinary formulation, 'point') is translated into 'ordered triple of real numbers'; 'P_3' ('plane') into 'class of ordered triples of real numbers fulfilling a linear equation', etc. The axioms, translated in this way, become C-true sentences of the mathematical calculus; hence the translation is C-true. On the basis of the customary interpretation of the mathematical calculus, the axioms and theorems of geometry become L-true propositions.

The difference between mathematical and physical geometry became clear in the historical development by the discovery of non-Euclidean geometry, i.e., of axiom systems deviating from the Euclidean form by replacing the parallel axiom (G 4) by some other axiom incompatible with it. It has been shown that each of these systems, although they are incompatible with one another, does not contain a contradiction, provided the Euclidean system is free from contradictions. This was shown by giving a translation for each of the non-Euclidean systems into the Euclidean system. Mathematicians regarded all these systems on a par, investigating any one indifferently. Physicists, on the other hand, could not accept this plurality of geometries; they asked: "Which one is true? Has the space of nature the Euclidean or one of the non-Euclidean structures?" It became clear by an analysis of the discussions that the mathematician and the physicist were talking about different things, although they themselves were not aware of this in the beginning. Mathematicians have to do with the geometrical calculus, and with respect to a calculus there is no question of truth and falsity. Physicists, however, are concerned with a theory of space, i.e., of the system of possible configurations and movements of bodies, hence with the interpretation of a geometrical calculus. When an interpretation of the specific signs is established—and, to a certain extent, this is a matter of choice—then each of the calculi yields a physical geometry as a theory with factual content. Since they are incompatible, at most one can be true (truth of a class of sentences [see § 6]). The theories are factual.

The truth conditions, determined by the interpretation, refer to facts. Therefore, it is the task of the physicist, and not of the mathematician, to find out whether a certain one among the theories is true, i.e., whether a certain geometrical structure is that of the space of nature. (Of course, the truth of a system of physical geometry, like that of any other universal factual sentence or theory, can never be known with absolute certainty but at best with a high degree of confirmation.) For this purpose, the physicist has to carry out experiments and to see whether the predictions made with the help of the theory under investigation, in connection with other theories confirmed and accepted previously, are confirmed by the observed results of the experiments. The accuracy of the answer found by the physicist is, of course, dependent upon the accuracy of the instruments available. The answer given by classical physics was that the Euclidean system of geometry is in accordance with the results of measurements, within the limits of the accuracy of observations. Modern physics has modified this answer in the general theory of relativity by stating that the Euclidean geometry describes the structure of space, though not exactly, yet with a degree of approximation sufficient for almost all practical purposes; a more exact description is given by a certain non-Euclidean system of geometry. Physical geometry is in its methods not fundamentally different from the other parts of physics. This will become still more obvious when we shall see how other parts of physics can also take the form of calculi (§ 23).

The doctrine concerning geometry acknowledged by most philosophers in the past century was that of Kant, saying that geometry consists of "synthetic judgments a priori", i.e., of sentences which have factual content but which, nevertheless, are independent of experience and necessarily true. Kant attributed the same character also to the sentences of arithmetic. Modern logical analysis of language, however, does not find any sentences at all of this character. We may assume that the doctrine is not to be understood as applying to the formulas of a calculus; there is no question of truth with respect to them because they are not assertions; in any case they are not synthetic (i.e., factual). The doctrine was obviously meant to apply to arithmetic and geometry as theories, i.e., interpreted systems, with their customary interpretations. Then, however, the propositions of arithemetic are, to be sure, independent of experience, but only because they do not concern experience or facts at all; they are L-true (analytic), not factual (synthetic). For geometry there is also, as mentioned before, the possibility of a logico-mathematical interpretation; by it the sentences of geometry get the same character as those of mathematics. On the basis of the customary interpretation, however, the sentences of geometry, as propositions of physical geometry, are indeed factual (synthetic), but dependent upon experience, empirical. The Kantian doctrine is based on a failure to distinguish between mathematical and physical geometry. It is to this distinction that Einstein refers in his well-known dictum: "So far as the theorems of mathematics are about reality they are not certain; and so far as they are certain they are not about reality."

The question is frequently discussed whether arithmetic and geometry, looked at from the logical and methodological point of view, have the same nature or not. Now we see that the answer depends upon whether the calculi or the interpreted systems are meant. There is no fundamental difference between arithmetic and geometry as calculi, nor with respect to their *possible* interpretations; for either calculus there are both logical and descriptive interpretations. If, however, we take the systems with their *customary* interpretation—arithmetic as the theory of numbers and geometry as the theory of physical space—then we find an important difference: the propositions of arithmetic are logical, L-true, and without factual content; those of geometry are descriptive, factual, and empirical.

23. Physical Calculi and Their Interpretations

The method described with respect to geometry can be applied likewise to any other part of physics: we can first construct a calculus and then lay down the interpretation intended in the form of semantical rules, yielding a physical theory as an interpreted system with factual content. The customary formulation of a physical calculus is such that it presupposes a logico-mathematical calculus as its basis, e.g., a calculus of real numbers in any of the forms discussed above (§ 18). To this basic calculus are added the specific primitive signs and the axioms, i.e., specific primitive sentences, of the physical calculus in question.

Thus, for instance, a calculus of mechanics of mass points can be constructed. Some predicates and functors (i.e., signs for functions) are taken as specific primitive signs, and the fundamental laws of mechanics as axioms. Then semantical rules are laid down stating that the primitive signs designate, say, the class of material particles, the three spatial coordinates of a particle x at the time t, the mass of a particle x, the class of forces acting on a particle x or at a space point s at the time t. (As we shall see later [§ 24], the interpretation can also be given indirectly, i.e., by semantical rules, not for the primitive signs, but for certain defined signs of the calculus. This procedure must be chosen if the semantical rules are to refer only to observable properties.) By the interpretation, the theorems of the calculus of mechanics become physical laws, i.e., universal statements describing certain features of events; they constitute physical mechanics as a theory with factual content which can be tested by observations. The relation of this theory to the calculus of mechanics is entirely analogous to the relation of physical to mathematical geometry. The customary division into theoretical and experimental physics corresponds roughly to the distinction between calculus and interpreted system. The work in theoretical physics consists mainly in constructing calculi and carrying out deductions within them; this is essentially mathematical work. In experimental physics interpretations are made and theories are tested by experiments.

In order to show by an example how a deduction is carried out with the help of a physical calculus, we will discuss a calculus which can be interpreted as a theory of thermic expansion. To the primitive signs may belong the predicates 'Sol' and

'Fe', and the functors 'lg', 'te', and 'th'. Among the axioms may be A 1 and A 2. (Here, 'x', 'β' and the letters with subscripts are real number variables; the parentheses do not contain explanations as in former examples, but are used as in algebra and for the arguments of functors.)

A 1. For every $x, t_1, t_2, l_1, l_2, T_1, T_2, \beta$ [if [x is a Sol and $\lg(x,t_1) = l_1$
and $\lg(x,t_2) = l_2$ and $\mathrm{te}(x,t_1) = T_1$ and $\mathrm{te}(x,t_2) = T_2$ and $\mathrm{th}(x) = \beta$]
then $l_2 = l_1 \times (1 + \beta \times (T_2 - T_1))$].

A 2. For every x, if [x is a Sol and x is a Fe] then $\mathrm{th}(x) = 0.000012$.

The *customary interpretation*, i.e., that for whose sake the calculus is constructed, is given by the following semantical rules. '$\lg(x,t)$' designates the length in centimeters of the body x at the time t (defined by the statement of a method of measurement); '$\mathrm{te}(x,t)$' designates the absolute temperature in centigrades of x at the time t (likewise defined by a method of measurement); '$\mathrm{th}(x)$' designates the coefficient of thermic expansion for the body x; 'Sol' designates the class of solid bodies; 'Fe' the class of iron bodies. By this interpretation, A 1 and A 2 become physical laws. A 1 is the law of thermic expansion in quantitative form, A 2 the statement of the coefficient of thermic expansion for iron. As A 2 shows, a statement of a physical constant for a certain substance is also a universal sentence. Further, we add semantical rules for two signs occuring in the subsequent example: the name 'c' designates the thing at such and such a place in our laboratory; the numerical variable 't' as time coordinate designates the time-point t seconds after August 17, 1938, 10:00 A.M.

Now we will analyze an example of a derivation within the calculus indicated. This derivation D_2 is, when interpreted by the rules mentioned, the deduction of a prediction from premisses giving the results of observations. The construction of the derivation D_2, however, is entirely independent of any interpretation. It makes use only of the rules of the calculus, namely, the physical calculus indicated together with a calculus of real numbers as basic calculus. We have discussed, but not written down, a similar derivation D_1 (§ 19), which, however, made use only of the mathematical calculus. Therefore the physical laws used had to be taken in D_1 as premisses. But here in D_2 they belong to the axioms of the calculus (A 1 and A 2, occurring as [6] and [10]). Any axiom or theorem proved in a physical calculus may be used within any derivation in that calculus without belonging to the premisses of the derivation, in exactly the same way in which a proved theorem is used within a derivation in a logical or mathematical calculus, e.g., in the first example of a derivation in § 19 sentence (7), and in D_1 (§ 19) the sentences which in D_2 are called (7) and (13). Therefore only singular sentences (not containing variables) occur as premisses in D_2. (For the distinction between premisses and axioms see the remark at the end of § 19.)

Derivation D_2:

Premisses
{
1. c is a Sol.
2. c is a Fe.
3. $te(c,0) = 300$.
4. $te(c,600) = 350$.
5. $lg(c,0) = 1,000$.
}

Axiom A 1

6. For every x, t_1, t_2, l_1, l_2, T_1, T_2, β [if [x is a Sol and $lg(x,t_1) = l_1$ and $lg(x,t_2) = l_2$ and $te(x,t_1) = T_1$ and $te(x,t_2) = T_2$ and $th(x) = \beta$] then $l_2 = l_1 \times (1 + \beta \times (T_2 - T_1))$].

Proved mathem. theorem:

7. For every l_1, l_2, T_1, T_2, β [$l_2 - l_1 = l_1 \times \beta \times (T_2 - T_1)$ if and only if $l_2 = l_1 \times (1 + \beta \times (T_2 - T_1))$].

(6)(7)

8. For every x, t_1, ... (as in [6]) ... [if [- - -] then $l_2 - l_1 = l_1 \times \beta \times (T_2 - T_1)$].

(1)(3)(4)(8)

9. For every l_1, l_2, β [if [$th(c) = \beta$ and $lg(c, 0) = l_1$ and $lg(c,600) = l_2$] then $l_2 - l_1 = l_1 \times \beta \times (350 - 300)$].

Axiom A 2

10. For every x, if [x is a Sol and x is a Fe] then $th(x) = 0.000012$.

(1)(2)(10)

11. $th(c) = 0.000012$.

(9)(11)(5)

12. For every l_1, l_2 [if [$lg(c,0) = l_1$ and $lg(c,600) = l_2$] then $l_2 - l_1 = 1,000 \times 0.000012 \times (350 - 300)$].

Proved mathem. theorem:

13. $1,000 \times 0.000012 \times (350 - 300) = 0.6$.

(12)(13) *Conclusion:* 14. $lg(c,600) - lg(c,0) = 0.6$.

On the basis of the interpretation given before, the premisses are singular sentences concerning the body c. They say that c is a solid body made of iron, that the temperature of c was at 10:00 A.M. 300° abs., and at 10:10 A.M. 350° abs., and that the length of c at 10:00 A.M. was 1,000 cm. The conclusion says that the increase in the length of c from 10:00 to 10:10 A.M. is 0.6 cm. Let us suppose that our measurements have confirmed the premisses. Then the derivation yields the conclusion as a prediction which may be tested by another measurement.

Any physical theory, and likewise the whole of physics, can in this way be presented in the form of an interpreted system, consisting of a specific calculus (axiom system) and a system of semantical rules for its interpretation; the axiom system is, tacitly or explicitly, based upon a logico-mathematical calculus with customary interpretation. It is, of course, logically possible to apply the same method to any other branch of science as well. But practically the situation is such that most of them seem at the present time to be not yet developed to a degree which would suggest this strict form of presentation. There is an interesting and successful attempt of an axiomatization of certain parts of biology, especially genetics, by Woodger (Vol. I, No. 10). Other scientific fields which we may expect to be soon accessible to this method are perhaps chemistry, economics, and some elementary parts of psychology and social science.

Within a physical calculus the mathematical and the physical theorems, i.e., C-true formulas, are treated on a par. But there is a fundamental difference between the corresponding *mathematical* and the *physical propositions* of the physical theory, i.e., the system with customary interpretation. This difference is often overlooked. That physical theorems are sometimes mistaken to be of the same nature as mathematical theorems is perhaps due to several factors, among them the fact that they contain mathematical symbols and numerical expressions and that they are often formulated incompletely in the form of a mathematical equation (e.g., A 1 simply in the form of the last equation occurring in it). A mathematical proposition may contain only logical signs, e.g., 'for every m, n, $m + n = n + m$', or descriptive signs also, if the mathematical calculus is applied in a descriptive system. In the latter case the proposition, although it contains signs not belonging to the mathematical calculus, may still be provable in this calculus, e.g., 'lg(c) + lg(d) = lg(d) + lg(c)' ('lg' designates length as before). A physical proposition always contains descriptive signs, because otherwise it could not have factual content; in addition, it usually contains also logical signs. Thus the difference between mathematical theorems and physical theorems in the interpreted system does not depend upon the kinds of signs occurring but rather on the kind of truth of the theorems. The truth of a mathematical theorem, even if it contains descriptive signs, is not dependent upon any facts concerning the designata of these signs. We can determine its truth if we know only the semantical rules; hence it is L-true. (In the example of the theorem just mentioned, we need not know the length of the body c.) The truth of a physical theorem, on the other hand, depends upon the properties of the designata of the descriptive signs occuring. In order to determine its truth, we have to make observations concerning these designata; the knowledge of the semantical rules is not sufficient. (In the case of A 2, e.g., we have to carry out experiments with solid iron bodies.) Therefore, a physical theorem, in contradistinction to a mathematical theorem, has factual content.

24. Elementary and Abstract Terms

We find among the concepts of physics—and likewise among those of the whole of empirical science—differences of abstractness. Some are more elementary than others, in the sense that we can apply them in concrete cases on the basis of observations in a more direct way than others. The others are more abstract; in order to find out whether they hold in a certain case, we have to carry out a more complex procedure, which, however, also finally rests on observations. Between quite elementary concepts and those of high abstraction there are many intermediate levels. We shall not try to give an exact definition for 'degree of abstractness'; what is meant will become sufficiently clear by the following series of sets of concepts, proceeding from elementary to abstract concepts: bright, dark, red, blue, warm, cold, sour, sweet, hard, soft (all concepts of this first set are meant as properties of things, not as sense-data); coincidence; length; length of time; mass, velocity, acceleration, density, pressure; temperature, quantity of heat; electric charge, electric current, electric field; electric potential, electric resistance, coefficient of induction, frequency of oscillation; wave function.

Suppose that we intend to construct an interpreted system of physics—or of the whole of science. We shall first lay down a calculus. Then we have to state semantical rules of the kind SD for the specific signs, i.e., for the physical terms. (The SL-rules are presupposed as giving the customary interpretation of the logico-mathematical basic calculus.) Since the physical terms form a system, i.e., are connected with one another, obviously we need not state a semantical rule for each of them. For which terms, then, must we give rules, for the elementary or for the abstract ones? We can, of course, state a rule for any term, no matter what its degree of abstractness, in a form like this: 'the term 'te' designates temperature', provided the metalanguage used contains a corresponding expression (here the word 'temperature') to specify the designatum of the term in question. But suppose we have in mind the following purpose for our syntactical and semantical description of the system of physics: the description of the system shall teach a layman to understand it, i.e., to enable him to apply it to his observations in order to arrive at explanations and predictions. A layman is meant as one who does not know physics but has normal senses and understands a language in which observable properties of things can be described (e.g., a suitable part of everyday non-scientific English). A rule like 'the sign 'P' designates the property of being blue' will do for the purpose indicated; but a rule like 'the sign 'Q' designates the property of being electrically charged' will not do. In order to fulfil the purpose, we have to give semantical rules for elementary terms only, connecting them with observable properties of things. For our further discussion we suppose the system to consist of rules of this kind, as indicated in the following diagram.

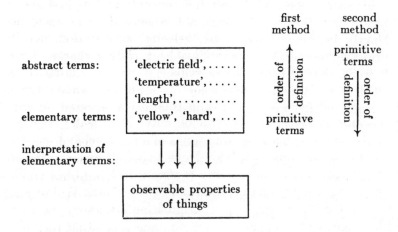

Now let us go back to the construction of the calculus. We have first to decide at which end of the series of terms to start the construction. Should we take elementary terms as primitive signs, or abstract terms? Our decision to lay down the semantical rules for the elementary terms does not decide this question. Either procedure is still possible and seems to have some reasons in its favor, depending on the point of view taken. The *first method* consists in taking elementary terms as primitive and then introducing on their basis further terms step by step, up to those of highest abstraction. In carrying out this procedure, we find that the introduction of further terms cannot always take the form of explicit definitions; conditional definitions must also be used (so-called reduction sentences [see Vol. I, No. 1, p. 50]). They describe a method of testing for a more abstract term, i.e., a procedure for finding out whether the term is applicable in particular cases, by referring to less abstract terms. The first method has the advantage of exhibiting clearly the connection between the system and observation and of making it easier to examine whether and how a given term is empirically founded. However, when we shift our attention from the terms of the system and the methods of empirical confirmation to the laws, i.e., the universal theorems, of the system, we get a different perspective. Would it be possible to formulate all laws of physics in elementary terms, admitting more abstract terms only as abbreviations? If so, we would have that ideal of a science in sensationalistic form which Goethe in his polemic against Newton, as well as some positivists, seems to have had in mind. But it turns out—this is an empirical fact, not a logical necessity— that it is not possible to arrive in this way at a powerful and efficacious system of laws. To be sure, historically, science started with laws formulated in terms of a low level of abstractness. But for any law of this kind, one nearly always later found some exceptions and thus had to confine it to a narrower realm of validity. The higher the physicists went in the scale of terms, the better did they succeed in formulating laws applying to a wide range of phenomena. Hence we understand that they are inclined to choose the *second method*. This method begins at the top of the system, so to speak, and then goes down to lower and lower levels. It consists in taking a few abstract terms as primitive signs and a few fundamental laws of great generality as axioms. Then further terms, less and less abstract, and finally elementary ones, are to be introduced by definitions; and here, so it seems at present, explicit definitions will do. More special laws, containing less abstract terms, are to be proved on the basis of the axioms. At least, this is the direction in which physicists have been striving with remarkable success, especially in the past few decades. But at the present time, the method cannot yet be carried through in the pure form indicated. For many less abstract terms no definition on the basis of abstract terms alone is as yet known; hence those terms must also be taken as primitive. And many more special laws, especially in biological fields, cannot yet be proved on the basis of laws in abstract terms only; hence those laws must also be taken as axioms.

Now let us examine the result of the interpretation if the first or the second method for the construction of the calculus is chosen. In both cases the semantical rules concern the elementary signs. In the first method these signs are taken as primitive. Hence, the semantical rules give a complete interpretation for these signs and those explicitly defined on their basis. There are, however, many signs, especially on the higher levels of abstraction, which can be introduced not by an explicit definition but only by a conditional one. The interpretation which the rules give for these signs is in a certain sense incomplete. This is due not to a defect in the semantical rules but to the method by which these signs are introduced; and this method is not arbitrary but corresponds to the way in which we really obtain knowledge about physical states by our observations.

If, on the other hand, abstract terms are taken as primitive—according to the second method, the one used in scientific physics—then the semantical rules have no direct relation to the primitive terms of the system but refer to terms introduced by long chains of definitions. The calculus is first constructed floating in the air, so to speak; the construction begins at the top and then adds lower and lower levels. Finally, by the semantical rules, the lowest level is anchored at the solid ground of the observable facts. The laws, whether general or special, are not directly interpreted, but only the singular sentences. For the more abstract terms, the rules determine only an *indirect interpretation*, which is—here as well as in the first method—incomplete in a certain sense. Suppose 'B' is defined on the basis of 'A'; then, if 'A' is directly interpreted, 'B' is, although indirectly, also interpreted completely; if, however, 'B' is directly interpreted, 'A' is not necessarily also interpreted completely (but only if 'A' is also definable by 'B').

To give an example, let us imagine a calculus of physics constructed, according to the second method, on the basis of primitive specific signs like 'electromagnetic field', 'gravitational field', 'electron', 'proton', etc. The system of definitions will then lead to elementary terms, e.g., to 'Fe', defined as a class of regions in which the configuration of particles fulfils certain conditions, and 'Na-yellow' as a class of space-time regions in which the temporal distribution of the electromagnetic field fulfils certain conditions. Then semantical rules are laid down stating that 'Fe' designates iron and 'Na-yellow' designates a specified yellow color. (If 'iron' is not accepted as sufficiently elementary, the rules can be stated for more elementary terms.) In this way the connection between the calculus and the realm of nature, to which it is to be applied, is made for terms of the calculus which are far remote from the primitive terms.

Let us examine, on the basis of these discussions, the example of a derivation D_2 (§ 23). The premisses and the conclusion of D_2 are singular sentences, but most of the other sentences are not. Hence the premisses and the conclusion of this as of all other derivations of the same type can be directly interpreted, understood, and confronted with the results of observations. More of an interpretation is not necessary for a practical application of a derivation. If, in confronting the interpreted premisses with our observations, we find them confirmed as true, then we accept the conclusion as a prediction and we may base a decision upon it. The sentences occurring in the derivation between premisses and conclusion are also interpreted, at least indirectly. But we need not make their interpretation explicit in order to be able to construct the derivation and to apply it. All that is necessary for its construction are the formal rules of the calculus. This is the advantage of the method of formalization, i.e., of the separation of the calculus as a formal system from the interpretation. If some persons want to come to an agreement about the formal correctness of a given derivation, they may leave aside all differences of opinion on material questions or questions of interpretation. They simply have to examine whether or not the given series of formulas fulfils the formal rules of the calculus. Here again, the function of calculi in empirical science becomes clear as instruments for transforming the expression of what we know or assume.

Against the view that for the application of a physical calculus we need an interpretation only for singular sentences, the following objection will perhaps be raised. Before we accept a derivation and believe its conclusion we must have accepted the physical calculus which furnishes the derivation; and how can we decide whether or not to accept a physical calculus for application without interpreting and understanding its axioms? To be sure, in order to pass judgment about the applicability of a given physical calculus we have to confront it in some way or other with observation, and for this purpose an interpretation is necessary. But we need no explicit interpretation of the axioms, nor even of any theorems. The empirical examination of a physical theory given in the form of a calculus with rules of interpretation is not made by interpreting and understanding the axioms and then considering whether they are true on the basis of our factual knowledge. Rather, the examination is carried out by the same procedure as that explained before for obtaining a prediction. We construct derivations in the calculus with premises which are singular sentences describing the results of our observations, and with singular sentences which we can test by observations as conclusions. The physical theory is indirectly confirmed to a higher and higher degree if more and more of these predictions are confirmed and none of them is disconfirmed by observations. Only singular sentences with elementary terms can be directly tested; therefore, we need an explicit interpretation only for these sentences.

25. "Understanding" in Physics

The development of physics in recent centuries, and especially in the past few decades, has more and more led to that method in the construction, testing, and application of physical theories which we call *formalization*, i.e., the construction of a calculus supplemented by an interpretation. It was the progress of knowledge and the particular structure of the subject matter that suggested and made practically possible this increasing formalization. In consequence it became more and more possible to forego an "intuitive understanding" of the abstract terms and axioms and theorems formulated with their help. The possibility and even necessity of abandoning the search for an understanding of that kind was not realized for a long time. When abstract, nonintuitive formulas, as, e.g., Maxwell's equations of electromagnetism, were proposed as new axioms, physicists endeavored to make them "intuitive" by constructing a "model", i.e., a way of representing electromagnetic microprocesses by an analogy to known macro-processes, e.g., movements of visible things. Many attempts have been made in this direction, but without satisfactory results. It is important to realize that the discovery of a model has no more than an aesthetic or didactic or at best a heuristic value, but is not at all essential for a successful application of the physical theory. The demand for an intuitive understanding of the axioms was less and less fulfilled when the development led to the general theory of relativity and then to quantum mechanics, involving the wave function. Many people, including physicists, have a feeling of regret and disappointment about this. Some, especially philosophers, go so far as even to contend that these modern theories, since they are not intuitively understandable, are not at all theories about nature but "mere formalistic constructions", "mere calculi". But this is a fundamental misunderstanding of the function of a physical theory. It is true a theory must not be a "mere calculus" but possess an interpretation, on the basis of which it can be applied to facts of nature. But it is sufficient, as we have seen, to make this interpretation explicit for elementary terms; the interpretation of the other terms is then indirectly determined by the formulas of the calculus, either definitions or laws, connecting them with the elementary terms. If we demand from the modern physicist an answer to the question what he means by the symbol 'ψ' of his calculus, and are astonished that he cannot give an answer, we ought to realize that the situation was already the same in classical physics. There the physicist could not tell us what he meant by the symbol 'E' in Maxwell's equations. Perhaps, in order not to refuse an answer, he would tell us that 'E' designates the electric field vector. To be sure, this statement has the form of a semantical rule, but it would not help us a bit to understand the theory. It simply refers from a symbol in a symbolic calculus to a corresponding word expression in a calculus of words. We are right in demanding an interpretation for 'E', but that will be given indirectly by semantical rules referring to elementary signs together with the formulas connecting them with 'E'. This interpretation enables us to use the laws containing 'E' for the derivation of predictions. Thus we understand 'E', if "understanding" of an expression, a sentence, or a theory means capability of its use for the description of known facts or the prediction of new facts. An "intuitive understanding" or a direct translation of 'E' into terms referring to observable properties is neither necessary nor possible. The situation of the modern physicist is not essentially different. He knows how to use the symbol 'ψ' in the calculus in order to derive predictions which we can test by observations. (If they have the form of probability statements, they are tested by statistical results of observations.) Thus the physicist, although he cannot give us a translation into everyday language, understands the symbol 'ψ' and the laws of quantum mechanics. He possesses that kind of understanding which alone is essential in the field of knowledge and science.

Selected Bibliography

CARNAP, R. *Abriss der Logistik.* Wien, 1929.

———. "Die Mathematik als Zweig der Logik," *Blätter für deutsche Philosophie*, Vol. IV (1930).

———. *Logical Syntax of Language.* (Orig., Wien, 1934.) London and New York, 1937.

———. "Formalwissenschaft und Realwissenschaft," *Erkenntnis*, Vol. V (1935).

———. "Testability and Meaning," *Philosophy of Science*, Vols. III (1936) and IV (1937).

DEDEKIND, R. *Was sind und was sollen die Zahlen?* Braunschweig, 1888.

EINSTEIN, A. *Geometrie and Erfahrung.* Berlin, 1921.

FRAENKEL, A. *Einleitung in die Mengenlehre.* 3d ed. Berlin, 1928.

FRANK, P. *Interpretations and Misinterpretations of Modern Physics.* Paris, 1938.

FREGE, G. *Die Grundlagen der Arithmetik.* Breslau, 1884.

———. *Grundgesetze der Arithmetik*, Vols. I and II. Jena, 1893 and 1903.

HAHN, H. *Logik, Mathematik und Naturerkennen.* Wien, 1933.

HEYTING, A. *Mathematische Grundlagenforschung, Intuitionismus, Beweistheorie.* Berlin, 1934.

HILBERT, D. "Axiomatisches Denken," *Math. Annalen*, Vol. LXXVIII (1918).

HILBERT, D., and ACKERMANN, W. *Grundzüge der theoretischen Logik.* Berlin, 1928. 2d ed., 1938.

HILBERT, D., and BERNAYS, P. *Grundlagen der Mathematik*, Vol. I. Berlin, 1934.

Foundations of Logic and Mathematics

LEWIS, C. I., and LANGFORD, C. H. *Symbolic Logic*. New York and London, 1932.

MENGER, K. "The New Logic," *Philosophy of Science*, Vol. IV (1937).

MORRIS, C. W. *Logical Positivism, Pragmatism, and Scientific Empiricism*. Paris, 1937.

PEIRCE, C. S. *Collected Papers* (esp. Vol II). Cambridge, Mass., 1931 ff.

QUINE, W. V. "Truth by Convention," in *Philosophical Essays for A. N. Whitehead*. London and New York, 1936.

REICHENBACH, H. *Philosophie der Raum-Zeit-Lehre*. Berlin, 1928.

RUSSELL, B. *The Principles of Mathematics*. Cambridge, 1903. 2d ed., 1938.

———. *Introduction to Mathematical Philosophy*. London, 1919. 2d ed., 1920.

SCHOLZ, H. *Geschichte der Logik*. Berlin, 1931.

TARSKI, A. "Der Wahrheitsbegriff in den formalisierten Sprachen," *Studia philosophica*, Vol. I (1935).

———. "Grundlegung der wissenschaftlichen Semantik," in *Actes du congrès international de philosophie scientifique*. Paris, 1936.

———. *Einführung in die mathematische Logik*. Wien, 1937.

WAISMANN, F. *Einführung in das mathematische Denken*. Wien, 1936.

WHITEHEAD, A. N. and RUSSELL, B. *Principia mathematica*, Vols. I, II, and III. Cambridge, (1910) 1925, (1912) 1927, and (1913) 1927.

WITTGENSTEIN, L. *Tractatus logico-philosophicus*. London, 1922.

Index of Terms

[The numbers refer to the sections of this monograph.]